Glencoe CHEMISTRY
MATTER AND CHANGE

Teaching Transparency Masters

 **Glencoe McGraw-Hill**

New York, New York   Columbus, Ohio   Woodland Hills, California   Peoria, Illinois

Glencoe
CHEMISTRY
MATTER AND CHANGE

Hands-On Learning:
Laboratory Manual, SE/TE
Forensics Laboratory Manual, SE/TE
CBL Laboratory Manual, SE/TE
Small-Scale Laboratory Manual, SE/TE
ChemLab and MiniLab Worksheets

Review/Reinforcement:
Study Guide for Content Mastery, SE/TE
Solving Problems: A Chemistry Handbook
Reviewing Chemistry
Guided Reading Audio Program

Applications and Enrichment:
Challenge Problems
Supplemental Problems

Assessment:
Chapter Assessment
MindJogger Videoquizzes (VHS/DVD)
TestCheck Software, Windows/MacIntosh

Teacher Resources:
Lesson Plans
Block Scheduling Lesson Plans
Spanish Resources
Section Focus Transparencies and Masters
Math Skills Transparencies and Masters
Teaching Transparencies and Masters
Solutions Manual

Technology:
Chemistry Interactive CD-ROM
Vocabulary PuzzleMaker Software,
    Windows/MacIntosh
Glencoe Science Web site:
science.glencoe.com

Send all inquiries to:
Glencoe/McGraw-Hill
8787 Orion Place
Columbus, OH 43240-4027

ISBN 0-07-824544-3
Printed in the United States of America.
3 4 5 6 7 8 9 10 081 09 08 07 06 05 04 03 02

Contents

To the Teacher

Teaching Transparency Masters includes black-and-white versions of the 80 full-color transparencies included in ***Chemistry: Matter and Change, Teaching Transparency Package***. These masters can be used to provide students with their own copies of the transparencies for making notes or to include in their chemistry notebooks for study and review. Each master is accompanied by a student worksheet, which helps you present, reinforce, or review key concepts developed in the text. Answers for the worksheets are provided at the back of the book.

TEACHING TRANSPARENCY MASTER

1

Earth's Atmosphere

**Use with Chapter 1,
Section 1.1**

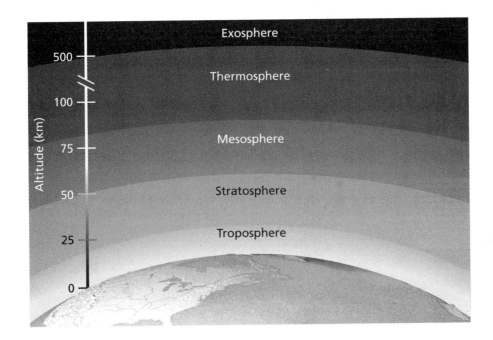

Name ______________________ Date ____________ Class ____________

TEACHING TRANSPARENCY WORKSHEET **1**

Earth's Atmosphere

Use with Chapter 1, Section 1.1

1. In which layer of Earth's atmosphere do commercial airplanes fly?

____

2. In which layer of Earth's atmosphere would you find the peaks of mountains?

____

3. In which layer of Earth's atmosphere would you find the ozone layer?

____

4. In which layer of Earth's atmosphere would you find the air you breathe?

____

5. In which layer of Earth's atmosphere does ozone form? Explain how it forms.

____

____

____

6. Over which region(s) of Earth are the highest concentrations of ozone found? Over which region(s) of Earth are the lowest concentrations of ozone found?

____

____

7. What is the source for the ultraviolet radiation in Earth's atmosphere?

____

8. How does ultraviolet radiation affect Earth's surface?

____

9. How does ultraviolet radiation affect humans and other organisms?

____

____

____

10. How does the ozone layer protect Earth from ultraviolet radiation?

____

____

TEACHING TRANSPARENCY MASTER

2

A Scientific Method

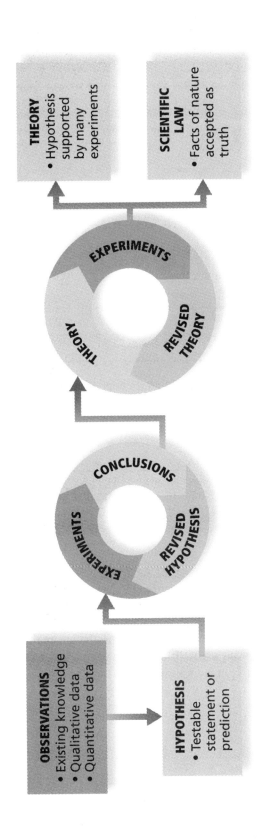

THEORY
• Hypothesis supported by many experiments

SCIENTIFIC LAW
• Facts of nature accepted as truth

EXPERIMENTS

THEORY

REVISED THEORY

CONCLUSIONS

EXPERIMENTS

REVISED HYPOTHESIS

OBSERVATIONS
• Existing knowledge
• Qualitative data
• Quantitative data

HYPOTHESIS
• Testable statement or prediction

TEACHING TRANSPARENCY WORKSHEET ②

A Scientific Method

Use with Chapter 1, Section 1.3

1. Define the term *scientific method*.

_____

_____

2. What is typically the first step in a scientific method? Give two examples.

_____

_____

3. What is a hypothesis?

_____

_____

4. Compare and contrast a hypothesis and a theory.

_____

_____

_____

5. Distinguish between an independent variable and a dependent variable.

_____

_____

_____

6. Suppose you observe that tadpoles hatched in stagnant water have a lower rate of survival than tadpoles hatched in water that is churned and aerated. Write a possible hypothesis you might test based on your observations. How might you test your hypothesis?

_____

_____

_____

7. You notice that when salt is sprinkled on an icy sidewalk, the ice melts even when the temperature is below freezing. Write a possible hypothesis you might test based on your observation. How might you test your hypothesis?

_____

_____

_____

TEACHING TRANSPARENCY MASTER ③

Laboratory Safety

Use with Chapter 1, Section 1.4

TEACHING TRANSPARENCY WORKSHEET ③

Laboratory Safety

Use with Chapter 1, Section 1.4

1. What should you do before entering the lab? List at least three things.

_____

_____

_____

2. What should you do if a chemical comes in contact with your skin?

_____

_____

3. When should you read the label on a chemical container?

_____

_____

_____

4. What is the proper way to prepare an acid solution?

_____

5. When should you wear safety goggles? Gloves?

_____

_____

_____

6. What kind of clothing should NOT be worn in the lab?

_____

_____

_____

7. What should you do when you have completed an assignment in the lab?

_____

_____

_____

Name _____ Date _____ Class _____

Converting Units

Use with Chapter 2, Section 2.2

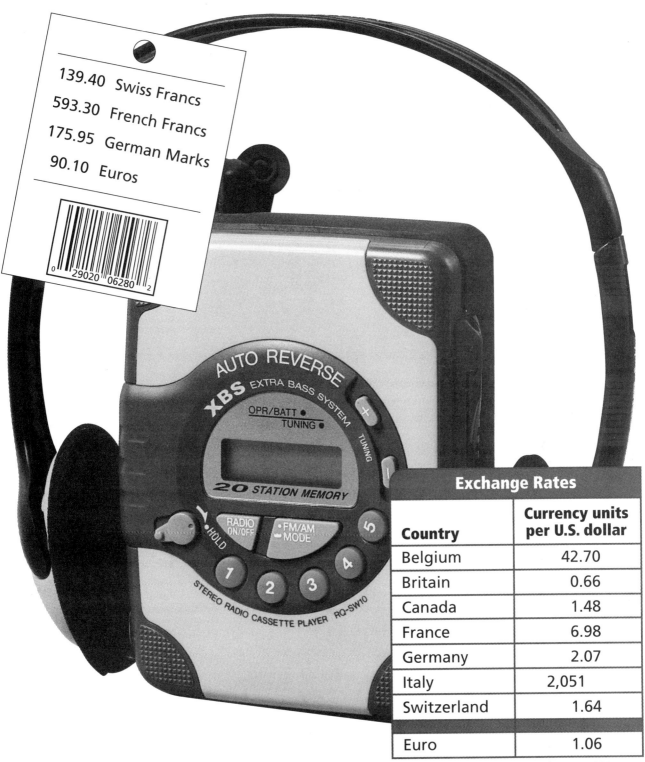

139.40 Swiss Francs

593.30 French Francs

175.95 German Marks

90.10 Euros

Exchange Rates	
Country	**Currency units per U.S. dollar**
Belgium	42.70
Britain	0.66
Canada	1.48
France	6.98
Germany	2.07
Italy	2,051
Switzerland	1.64
Euro	1.06

Source: *The Economist*, July 15, 2000

TEACHING TRANSPARENCY WORKSHEET   **4**

Converting Units

Use with Chapter 2,
Section 2.2

Exchange rates fluctuate daily. The ones shown on the transparency are for July 15,
2000. Show your work when necessary.

1. How much does the portable radio cassette player cost in U.S. dollars?

_____

_____

2. Which currency listed is closest to the value of the U.S. dollar?

_____

3. Assume that you have only British pounds. How many pounds would the portable radio
cassette player cost? Show your work.

_____

4. While traveling in Germany and France, you buy ice cream cones. The French cones sell
for 10 French francs. The German cones sell for 1.25 German marks. Which cone costs
you more U.S. dollars?

_____

_____

Suppose on January 15, 2001, the exchange rates have changed
as shown to the right. Use these exchange rates to answer
questions 5 and 6. Show your work when necessary.

5. A video game costs 570 French francs on January 15, 2001.
What is its price in U.S. dollars? Has the price risen or dropped
since July 15, 2000?

_____

_____

_____

6. A department store has stores in both Germany and in
Switzerland. A Swiss shopper pays 12 Swiss francs for a
candle. A German shopper pays 12 German marks for the
identical candle.

a. Which shopper gets the better deal?

_____

_____

b. What is the advantage of using the euro in both Germany
and Switzerland?

_____

Exchange Rates	
Country	**Currency units per U.S. dollar**
Belgium	42.95
Britain	0.71
Canada	1.37
France	6.51
Germany	2.09
Italy	2,085
Switzerland	1.61
Euro	1.02

TEACHING TRANSPARENCY MASTER ⑤

Precision and Accuracy

Use with Chapter 2,
Section 2.3

Super Fun Mini-Golf Course

Hole	1	2	3	4	5	6	7	8	9	Score	10	11	12	13	14	15	16	17	18	Score	Total Score
Par	5	4	4	4	3	5	4	3	4	36	4	3	5	4	4	4	3	5	4	36	72
Marguerite	6	6	6	6	5	6	6	5	6	52	6	6	6	6	6	6	5	6	5	52	104
Jon	8	3	7	4	2	4	8	6	3	45	7	6	4	4	7	3	5	8	3	46	92
Anne-Marie	4	4	4	4	4	5	4	3	4	36	4	4	5	4	4	4	3	5	4	37	73
Shegecki	3	6	3	4	2	7	3	2	8	38	3	2	4	7	3	3	2	4	6	34	72

TEACHING TRANSPARENCY WORKSHEET

Precision and Accuracy

Use with Chapter 2,
Section 2.3

In golf, a player tries to use the fewest swings, or strokes, of a club to hit a ball into a series of holes. The player keeps score by counting the number of strokes used for each hole. The player's final score is the total number of strokes. The lower the number of strokes used, the better the score.

Par is a term that refers to the target score for a particular hole. It is the number of strokes that a player is expected to use to hit the ball into that hole. A player's accuracy is related to how closely his or her score comes to par. The closer a player's score is to par, the more accurate the player. A player's precision refers to the consistency of his or her score in comparison with par. A player whose score deviates consistently from par at each hole is more precise than one whose score deviates inconsistently.

1. Which player's overall game was most accurate?

_____

2. Which player's overall game was both accurate and precise?

_____

3. Use the terms *accurate* and *precise* to describe Marguerite's overall game.

_____

4. Which player seems to be neither accurate nor precise in his or her golf play?

_____

5. At the end of a golf game, which is more important: precision or accuracy?
Explain your answer.

_____

_____

_____

_____

6. Compare and contrast the results of a golf game to the data from an experiment.

_____

_____

_____

_____

_____

Name _____ Date _____ Class _____

Interpreting Graphs

Use with Chapter 2, Section 2.4

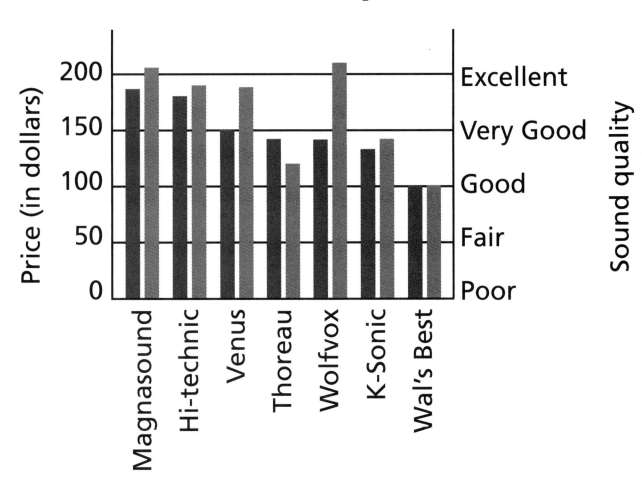

Brands of Stereo Speakers

■ Sound quality
▨ Price

Name ______________________ Date ____________ Class ____________

TEACHING TRANSPARENCY WORKSHEET 6

Interpreting Graphs

Use with Chapter 2, Section 2.4

1. What kind of graph is this?

____

2. What variables are compared in the graph?

____

3. Which product has the best sound quality? Which has the poorest sound quality?

____

4. Which product costs the most? The least?

____

5. If there are no limits on the amount of money you can spend, which product would you buy? Why?

____

____

6. If you can spend only $120, which product would you buy? Why?

____

____

7. If you can spend up to $200, which product would you buy? Why?

____

____

____

8. Which product is the best deal? Which is the worst deal?

____

____

____

____

____

____

____

States of Matter

Use with Chapter 3,
Section 3.1

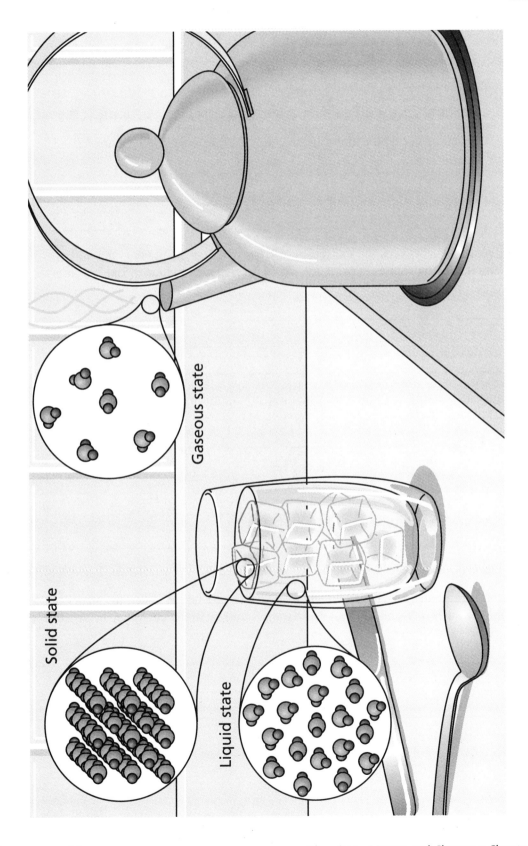

Gaseous state

Solid state

Liquid state

TEACHING TRANSPARENCY WORKSHEET

States of Matter

**Use with Chapter 3,
Section 3.1**

1. Name the physical states in which almost all matter exists.

   _____

2. In which state(s) of matter are the molecules most compressed?

   _____

3. In which state(s) of matter do the molecules fill the entire volume of a container?

   _____

4. In which state(s) does matter take the shape of a container?

   _____

5. Compare the distance between the molecules of a gas in a very small container with the distance between the molecules of the same gas in a very large container. Explain your answer.

   _____

   _____

   _____

6. What happens to the volume of a liquid when it is poured from a small container into a large container?

   _____

7. Suppose you fill a glass with ice cubes. When the ice cubes melt, is the glass still full? Explain your answer.

   _____

   _____

   _____

8. Suppose you fill a container with steam and then seal the container. When the steam in the container changes to liquid water at room temperature, will the container still be full? Explain your answer.

   _____

   _____

   _____

Name _____ Date _____ Class _____

Conservation of Mass

Use with Chapter 3,
Sections 3.2

Name ______________________ Date ____________ Class ____________

TEACHING TRANSPARENCY WORKSHEET 8

Conservation of Mass

Use with Chapter 3, Sections 3.2

1. What happens when mercury(II) oxide is heated?

____

____

2. What does the law of conservation of mass state?

____

3. Write the law of conservation of mass in mathematical terms.

____

4. Assume that the test tube shown in the transparency started out having 15.00 g of mercury(II) oxide. After heating the test tube, you find no mercury(II) oxide left and 1.11 g of oxygen gas. What mass of liquid mercury was produced by the chemical reaction? Show your work.

____

____

____

____

5. Assume that the test tube shown started out having 10.00 g of mercury(II) oxide. After heating the test tube briefly, you find 1.35 g mercury(II) oxide left and 8.00 g of liquid mercury. How much oxygen gas was produced by the chemical reaction? Show your work.

____

____

____

____

6. Suppose you heat some mercury(II) oxide in a test tube similar to the one shown. After the chemical reaction, you find 12.5 g of liquid mercury and 1.0 g of oxygen gas. There is no mercury(II) oxide left in the test tube. How much mercury(II) oxide did you start with? Show your work.

____

____

____

____

Name _____ Date _____ Class _____

Types of Matter

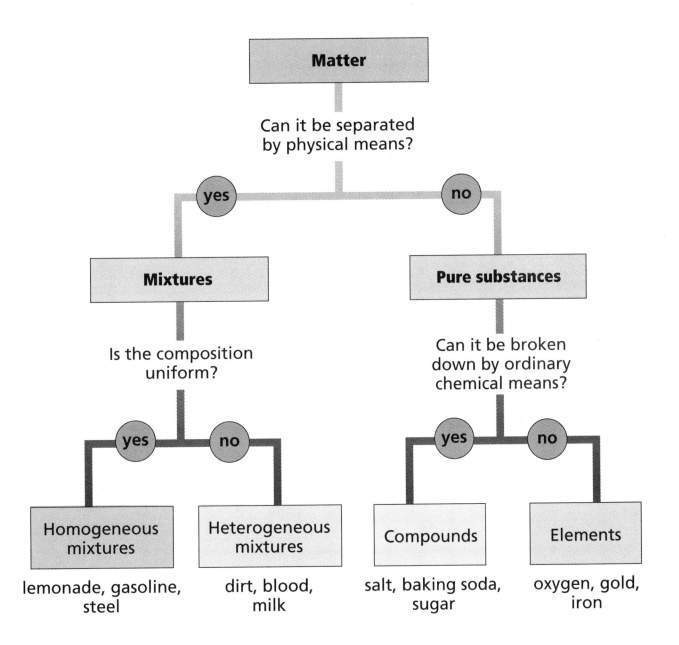

Matter	
Can it be separated by physical means?	

yes → **Mixtures** — Is the composition uniform?

no → **Pure substances** — Can it be broken down by ordinary chemical means?

Mixtures:
- yes → **Homogeneous mixtures** — lemonade, gasoline, steel
- no → **Heterogeneous mixtures** — dirt, blood, milk

Pure substances:
- yes → **Compounds** — salt, baking soda, sugar
- no → **Elements** — oxygen, gold, iron

TEACHING TRANSPARENCY WORKSHEET

Types of Matter

**Use with Chapter 3,
Section 3.4**

1. Into what two broad classes can all matter be divided?

_____

2. What is the difference between a mixture and a pure substance?

_____

_____

3. What is the difference between a compound and an element?

_____

_____

4. Can a compound be a heterogeneous mixture? Explain your answer by referring to the diagram.

_____

_____

_____

5. A list of compounds and elements is given below. Circle the substances that are elements.

gold	aluminum	water
sugar	oxygen	platinum
salt	chlorine	brass

6. How can you tell the difference between a homogeneous mixture and a heterogeneous mixture?

_____

_____

_____

7. Label each mixture below as either homogeneous or heterogeneous.

a. air _____

b. clay _____

c. homemade lemonade (with pulp) _____

d. oatmeal raisin cookie _____

e. finger paint _____

f. vinegar _____

g. soil _____

8. List three methods that are commonly used to separate mixtures into their component substances.

_____

_____

Mass Percentage and the Law of Definite Proportions

Use with Chapter 3, Section 3.4

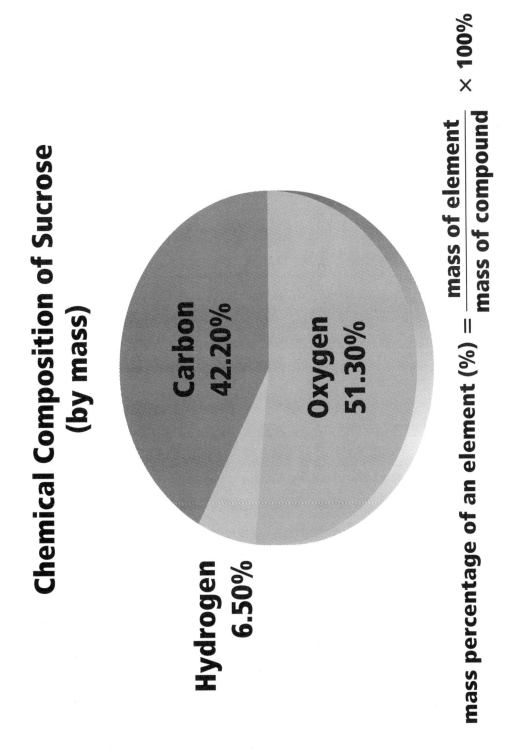

Chemical Composition of Sucrose (by mass)

Carbon 42.20%

Oxygen 51.30%

Hydrogen 6.50%

$$\text{mass percentage of an element (\%)} = \frac{\text{mass of element}}{\text{mass of compound}} \times 100\%$$

Name ______________________ Date ____________ Class ____________

TEACHING TRANSPARENCY WORKSHEET **10**

Mass Percentage and the Law of Definite Proportions

Use with Chapter 3, Section 3.4

1. Suppose you analyze the composition of an unnamed compound. Your analysis shows that the compound is 51.30% oxygen, 42.20% carbon, and 6.50% hydrogen by mass. What can you conclude about the compound?

____

2. What is the mass percentage of carbon in 5.000 g of sucrose? 50.00 g of sucrose? 500.0 g of sucrose? Explain.

____

____

3. How many grams of oxygen are in 50.00 g of sucrose? Show your work.

____

____

____

4. How many grams of carbon are in 100.0 g of sucrose? Show your work.

____

____

____

5. How many grams of hydrogen are in 6.0 g of sucrose? Show your work.

____

____

____

7. A 20.00-g sample of ordinary table salt contains 12.13 g of chlorine and 7.87 g of sodium. Calculate the mass percentage of each element in salt.

____

____

____

8. Draw a circle graph to represent your answer to question 7.

TEACHING TRANSPARENCY MASTER

Cathode Ray Experiments

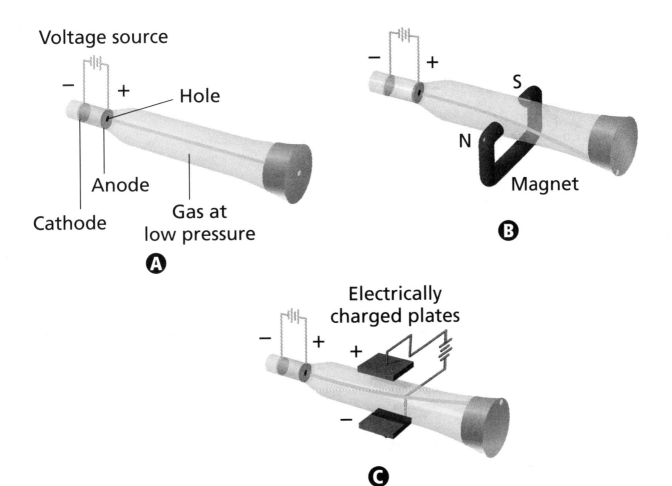

Voltage source

Hole

Anode

Cathode

Gas at
low pressure

A

S

N

Magnet

B

Electrically
charged plates

C

TEACHING TRANSPARENCY WORKSHEET

Cathode Ray Experiments

**Use with Chapter 4,
Section 4.2**

1. What is a cathode ray?

_____

2. What do the experiments in A, B, and C have in common?

_____

_____

_____

3. Examine the cathode ray experiment in A. Describe the path of the cathode ray from its origin to its termination.

_____

_____

_____

4. Compare the experimental setup in B with the setup in C. How do the two setups differ? What do both experiments show in terms of the cathode ray's charge?

_____

_____

_____

5. Examine the cathode ray experiment in B. What does this experiment show?

_____

_____

6. Examine the cathode ray experiment in C. Explain why the cathode ray bends.

_____

_____

Understanding Rutherford's Gold Foil Experiment

Use with Chapter 4, Section 4.2

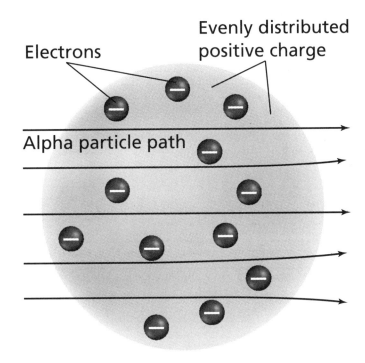

Diagram A

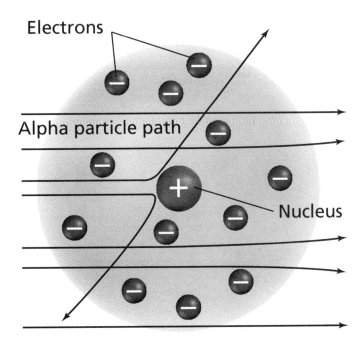

Diagram B

Name _____ Date _____ Class _____

TEACHING TRANSPARENCY WORKSHEET 12

Understanding Rutherford's Gold Foil Experiment

Use with Chapter 4, Section 4.2

1. What kind of particles do the arrows represent? What is the charge of the particles?

_____

2. Which diagram depicts the plum pudding model of an atom?

_____

3. Which diagram depicts Rutherford's actual results from his gold foil experiment? How did the actual results differ from the expected results?

_____

4. What did Rutherford conclude from the results of his experiment?

_____

_____

_____

_____

5. Explain why Rutherford expected the alpha particles to pass through the plum pudding model of the atom with little or no deflection.

_____

_____

_____

TEACHING TRANSPARENCY MASTER

13

Isotopes

Use with Chapter 4, Section 4.3

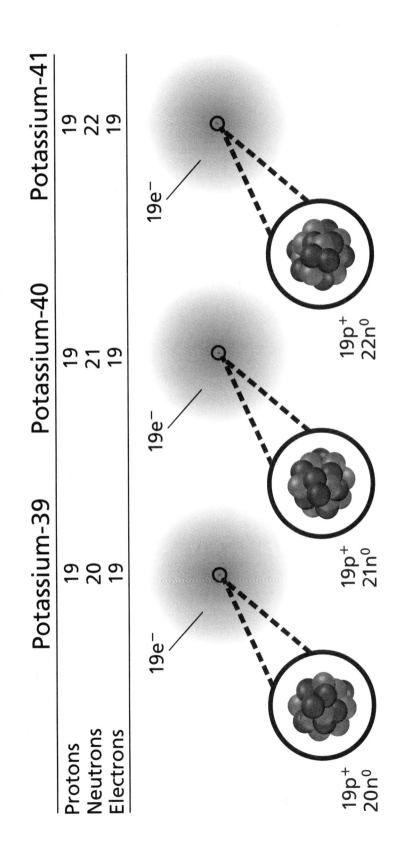

	Potassium-39	Potassium-40	Potassium-41
Protons	19	19	19
Neutrons	20	21	22
Electrons	19	19	19

19e$^-$

19e$^-$

19e$^-$

19p$^+$
20n^0

19p$^+$
21n^0

19p$^+$
22n^0

TEACHING TRANSPARENCY WORKSHEET ⑬

Isotopes

**Use with Chapter 4,
Section 4.3**

1. What do the following symbols represent?

    a. e^- _____

    b. n^0 _____

    c. p^+ _____

2. Which subatomic particles are found in an atom's nucleus?

_____

3. Which subatomic particle identifies an atom as that of a particular element?

_____

4. Explain why atoms are neutral even though they contain charged particles.

_____

_____

5. What do the numbers 39, 40, and 41 after the element name potassium refer to?

_____

_____

6. Write the symbolic notation for each of the following isotopes.

    a. potassium-39 _____

    b. potassium-40 _____

    c. potassium-41 _____

7. Write an equation showing the relationship between an atom's atomic number and its mass number.

_____

8. Lithium has two isotopes: lithium-6 and lithium-7. Draw a diagram, like those shown on the transparency, for each lithium isotope. Label the protons, electrons, neutrons, and electron cloud in each diagram.

_____

_____

_____

_____

Name _____ Date _____ Class _____

Radioactive Particles

Use with Chapter 4, Section 4.4

Characteristics of Alpha, Beta, and Gamma Radiation

Radiation Type	Composition	Symbol	Mass (amu)	Charge
Alpha	Helium nuclei (alpha particles)	$^{4}_{2}He$	4	2+
Beta	Electrons (beta particles)	$^{0}_{-1}\beta$	1/1840	1−
Gamma	High-energy electromagnetic radiation	$^{0}_{0}\gamma$	0	0

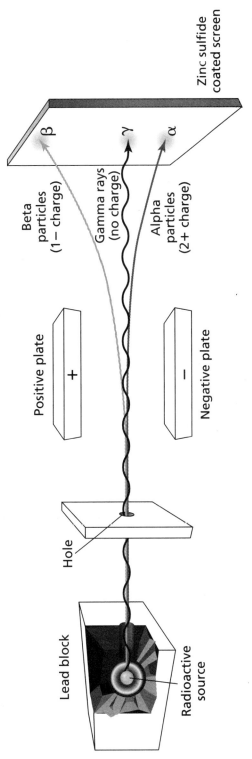

TEACHING TRANSPARENCY WORKSHEET

Radioactive Particles

**Use with Chapter 4,
Section 4.4**

1. Which radioactive emission has the greatest mass? Least mass?

_____

2. Why do you think gamma rays are drawn as wavy lines?

_____

_____

3. Which charged plate are the alpha particles attracted to? Explain.

_____

_____

4. Which charged plate are the beta particles attracted to? Why do the beta particles have a greater curvature than the alpha particles do?

_____

_____

_____

5. Explain why the gamma rays do not bend toward one of the electrically charged plates.

_____

_____

TEACHING TRANSPARENCY MASTER **15**

The Electromagnetic Spectrum

**Use with Chapter 5,
Section 5.1**

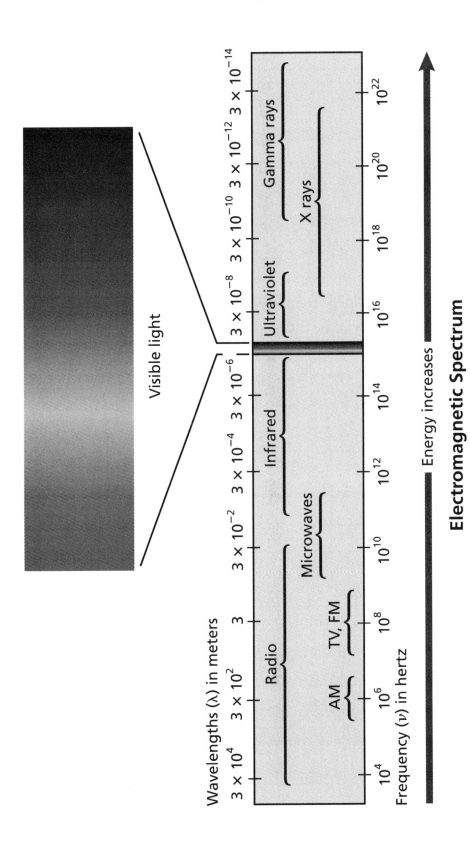

TEACHING TRANSPARENCY WORKSHEET (15)

The Electromagnetic Spectrum

**Use with Chapter 5,
Section 5.1**

1. What kinds of waves have the longest wavelength? What kinds of waves have the shortest wavelength?

_____

2. Which waves have the lowest frequency?

_____

3. Which has a higher frequency: microwaves or X rays?

_____

4. Which waves can be seen by the eye?

_____

_____

5. Sequence the different segments of the visible spectrum in order from shortest wavelength to longest wavelength.

_____

6. Sequence the following types of waves from lowest frequency to highest frequency: ultraviolet rays, infrared rays, gamma rays, radio waves, and green light.

_____

7. Compare the wavelengths and frequencies of each kind of wave. What is the relationship between frequency and wavelength?

_____

_____

_____

8. What is the wavelength of a radio station emitting its signal at 95.5 MHz? Estimate your answer to the nearest power of ten.

_____

Name _____ Date _____ Class _____

Atomic Orbitals

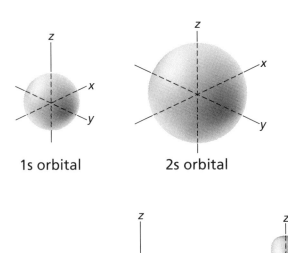

1s orbital   2s orbital

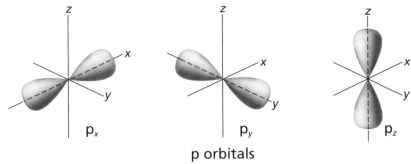

p_x p_y p_z

p orbitals

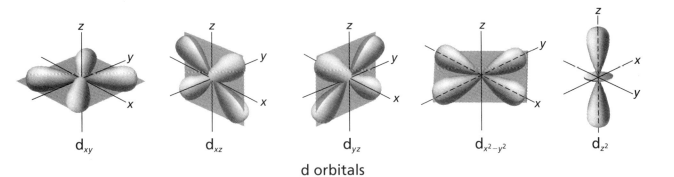

d_{xy} d_{xz} d_{yz} $d_{x^2-y^2}$ d_{z^2}

d orbitals

TEACHING TRANSPARENCY WORKSHEET

Atomic Orbitals

**Use with Chapter 5,
Section 5.2**

1. What is the shape of an s orbital?

_____

2. What is the relationship between the size of an s orbital and the principal energy level in
which it is found?

_____

_____

3. What is the shape of a p orbital? How many p orbitals are there in a sublevel?

_____

_____

4. How many electrons can each orbital hold?

_____

5. Look at the diagrams of the p orbitals. What do *x*, *y*, and *z* refer to?

_____

_____

6. How many d orbitals are there in a given sublevel? How many total electrons can the
d orbitals in a sublevel hold?

_____

_____

7. Which d orbitals have the same shape?

_____

8. What point in each diagram represents an atom's nucleus?

_____

_____

9. How likely is it that an electron occupying a p or a d orbital would be found very near an
atom's nucleus? What part of the diagram supports your conclusion?

_____   _____

_____

_____

Orbital Filling Sequence and Energy Levels

**Use with Chapter 5,
Section 5.3**

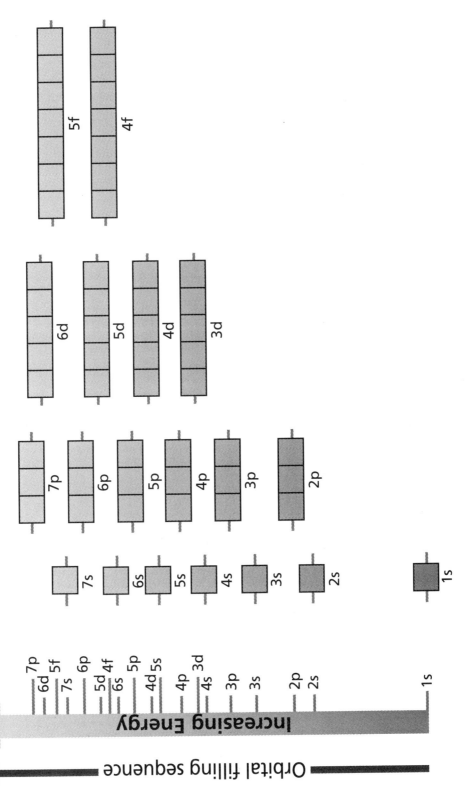

Name ______________________________ Date ______________ Class ______________

TEACHING TRANSPARENCY WORKSHEET **17**

Orbital Filling Sequence and Energy Levels

Use with Chapter 5, Section 5.3

1. What does each small box in the diagram represent?

2. How many electrons can each orbital hold?

3. How many electrons can the d sublevel hold?

4. Which is associated with more energy: a 2s or a 2p orbital?

5. Which is associated with more energy: a 2s or a 3s orbital?

6. According to the aufbau principle, which orbital should fill first, a 4s or a 3d orbital?

7. Which orbital has the least amount of energy?

8. What is the likelihood that an atom contains a 1s orbital?

9. Sequence the following orbitals in the order that they should fill up according to the aufbau principle: 4d, 4p, 4f, 5s, 6s, 5p, 3d, 4s.

10. Write a general rule to describe the filling of orbitals in an atom.

TEACHING TRANSPARENCY MASTER

The Periodic Table

Use with Chapter 6,
Section 6.1

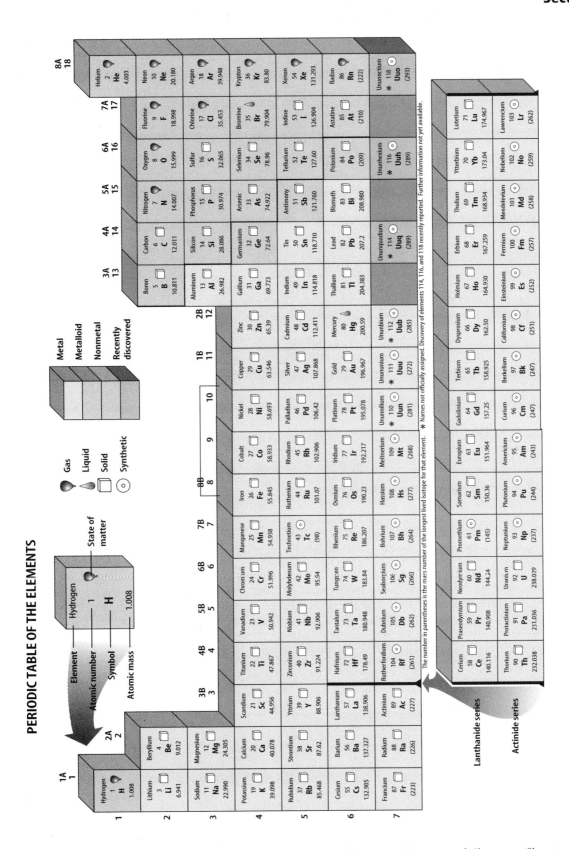

TEACHING TRANSPARENCY WORKSHEET

18

The Periodic Table

**Use with Chapter 6,
Section 6.1**

1. How many elements are listed in the periodic table? _____

2. What is the atomic number of selenium? _____

3. What is the symbol for palladium? _____

4. What is the atomic mass of strontium? _____

5. How are elements that are gases at room temperature designated in the periodic table?

_____

6. How many columns of elements does the periodic table contain? _____

7. What is another name for a column of elements?

_____

8. What two group numbers can be used to designate elements in the second column of the periodic table?

_____

9. How many rows of elements does the periodic table contain? _____

10. What is another name for a row of elements? _____

11. Which period contains the least number of elements? _____

12. What element is found in period 4, group 7B? _____

13. How are metals designated in the periodic table?

_____

14. How are metalloids designated in the periodic table?

_____

15. How are nonmetals designated in the periodic table?

_____

16. What is the name of the group 1A elements (excluding hydrogen)? _____

17. What is the name of the group 2A elements? _____

18. What is the name of the group 7A elements? _____

19. What is the name of the group 8A elements? _____

20. What can be said about the electron configurations of all the elements in a group?

_____

Name _____ Date _____ Class _____

The s-, p-, d-, and f-Block Elements

**Use with Chapter 6,
Section 6.2**

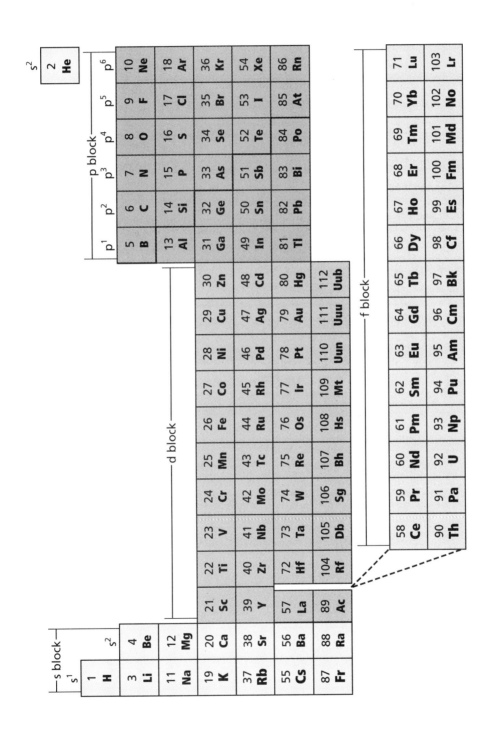

The s-, p-, d-, and f-Block Elements

Use with Chapter 6, Section 6.2

1. What are the four sections, or blocks, of the periodic table? _____

2. What does each block represent?

_____

3. What do elements in the s-block have in common?

_____

4. What is the valence electron configuration of each element in group 1A? _____

5. What is the valence electron configuration of each element in group 2A? _____

6. Why does the s-block span two groups of elements?

_____

7. Why does the p-block span six groups of elements?

_____

_____

_____

8. Why are there no p-block elements in period 1?

_____

_____

9. What is the ending of the electron configuration of each element in group 4A? _____

10. What is the electron configuration of neon? _____

11. In what period does the first d-energy sublevel appear? _____

12. Why does the d-block span ten groups of elements?

_____

_____

13. What is the ending of the electron configuration of each element in group 3B? _____

14. What is the electron configuration of titanium? _____

15. In what period does the first f-energy sublevel appear? _____

16. Determine the group, period, and block for the element having the electron configuration
    $[Xe]4f^{14}5d^{10}6s^26p^3$.

    a. group _____   **b.** period _____   **c.** block _____

Name _____ Date _____ Class _____

Atomic and Ionic Radii

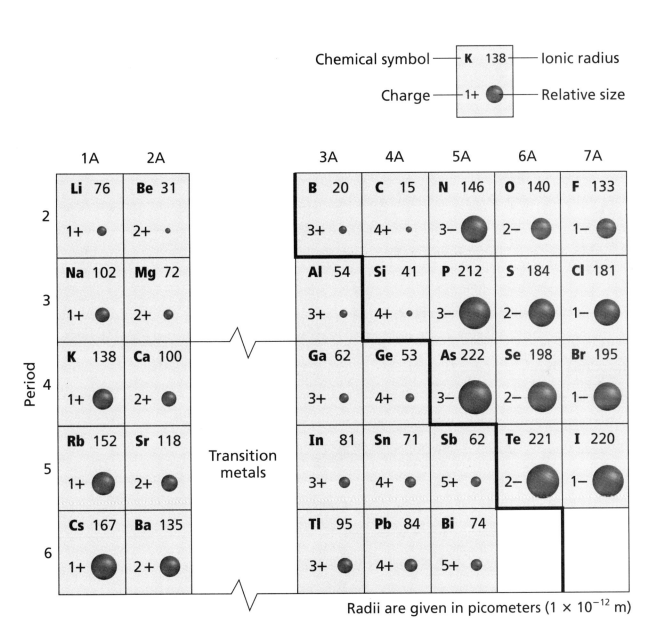

Radii are given in picometers (1×10^{-12} m)

Name _____ Date _____ Class _____

Atomic and Ionic Radii

**Use with Chapter 6,
Section 6.3**

1. Which groups and periods of elements are shown in the table of atomic radii?

_____

2. In what unit is atomic radius measured? Express this unit in scientific notation.

_____

3. What are the values of the smallest and largest atomic radii shown? What elements have these atomic radii?

_____

4. What happens to atomic radii within a period as the atomic number increases?

_____

_____

5. Cite any exceptions to the generalization you stated in your answer to question 4.

_____

_____

6. What accounts for the trend in atomic radii within a period?

_____

_____

_____

7. What happens to atomic radii within a group as the atomic number increases?

_____

_____

8. Cite any exceptions to the generalization you stated in your answer to question 7.

_____

9. What accounts for the trend in atomic radii within a group?

_____

_____

_____

10. In the table of ionic radii, how is the charge of the ions of elements in groups 1A–4A related to the group number of the elements?

_____

Name _____   Date _____   Class _____

First Ionization and Successive Ionization Energies

Use with Chapter 6, Section 6.3

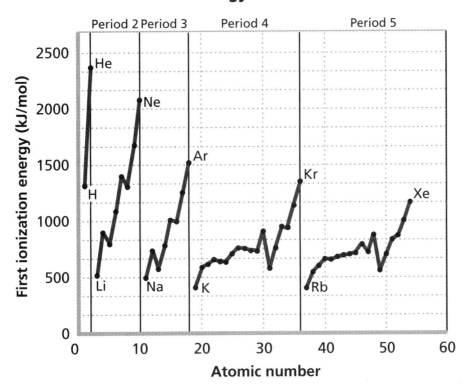

First Ionization Energy of Elements in Periods 1–5

Successive Ionization Energies for the Period 2 Elements

Element	Valence electrons	Ionization energy (kJ/mol)*								
		1st	2nd	3rd	4th	5th	6th	7th	8th	9th
Li	1	520	7300							
Be	2	900	1760	14 850						
B	3	800	2430	3660	25 020					
C	4	1090	2350	4620	6220	37 830				
N	5	1400	2860	4580	7480	9440	53 270			
O	6	1310	3390	5300	7470	10 980	13 330	71 330		
F	7	1680	3370	6050	8410	11 020	15 160	17 870	92 040	
Ne	8	2080	3950	6120	9370	12 180	15 240	20 000	23 070	115 380

* mol is an abbreviation for mole, a quantity of matter.

TEACHING TRANSPARENCY WORKSHEET **21**

First Ionization and Successive Ionization Energies

Use with Chapter 6, Section 6.3

1. What is meant by first ionization energy?

_____

_____

2. Which element has the smallest first ionization energy? The largest? What are their values?

_____

3. What generally happens to the first ionization energy of the elements within a period as the atomic number of the elements increases?

_____

_____

4. What accounts for the general trend in the first ionization energy of the elements within a period?

_____

_____

_____

5. What happens to the values of the successive ionization energies of an element?

_____

6. Based on the graph, rank the group 2A elements in periods 1–5 in decreasing order of first ionization energy.

_____

7. How is a jump in ionization energy related to the valence electrons of the element?

_____

8. What generally happens to the first ionization energy of the elements within a group as the atomic number of the elements increases?

_____

_____

9. What accounts for the general trend in the first ionization energy of the elements within a group?

_____

_____

_____

TEACHING TRANSPARENCY MASTER

Elements in Food

**Use with Chapter 7,
Section 7.1**

Element	Function	Food Source
Calcium	formation of bones and teeth, blood clotting, normal muscle and nerve activity	milk, cheese, nuts, whole grains
Phosphorus	formation of bones and teeth, regulation of blood pH, muscle contraction and nerve activity, in molecules that control release of energy	milk, whole-grain cereals, meats, vegetables
Iron	component of hemoglobin (carries oxygen to body cells) and heredity	liver, egg yolk, peas, enriched cereals, whole grains, meat, raisins, leafy vegetables
Iodine	required by thyroid gland, which controls growth	seafood, eggs, milk, iodized table salt
Sodium	transmission of nerve impulses	bacon, butter, table salt, vegetables
Potassium	transmission of nerve impulses, muscle contraction	vegetables, bananas, ketchup, fish
Magnesium	muscle and nerve function, bone formation, control of reaction rates in cells	potatoes, fruits, whole-grain cereals, vegetables
Fluorine	tooth structure	fluoridated water
Manganese	helps activate release of energy from carbohydrates, proteins, and fats; important in growth of cartilage and bone tissue	wheat germ, nuts, bran, leafy green vegetables

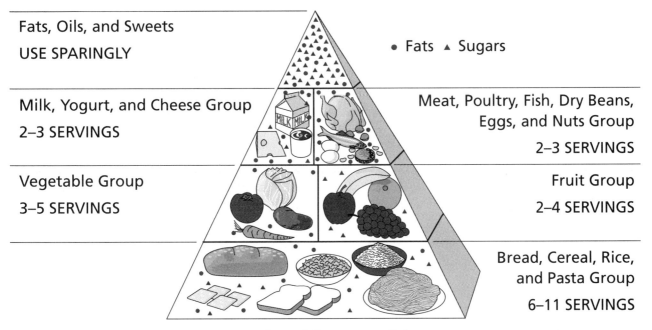

Fats, Oils, and Sweets
USE SPARINGLY

• Fats ▲ Sugars

Milk, Yogurt, and Cheese Group
2–3 SERVINGS

Meat, Poultry, Fish, Dry Beans, Eggs, and Nuts Group
2–3 SERVINGS

Vegetable Group
3–5 SERVINGS

Fruit Group
2–4 SERVINGS

Bread, Cereal, Rice, and Pasta Group
6–11 SERVINGS

Food Guide Pyramid

TEACHING TRANSPARENCY WORKSHEET   (22)

Elements in Food

Use with Chapter 7,
Section 7.1

1. Which elements listed in the chart are alkali metals? _____

2. Which elements listed in the chart are alkaline earth metals? _____

3. Which elements in the chart are involved in the following body functions?

   a. activity of nervous system _____

   b. bone formation _____

   c. activity of muscles _____

4. The Food Guide Pyramid shows the numbers of servings of different food groups that
   people should eat every day to ensure they are getting the right amounts of nutrients. Use
   the Food Guide Pyramid to write a breakfast, lunch, and dinner menu for a single day that
   includes the recommended numbers of servings of the different food groups. Write your
   menu below. Identify the food group and the number of servings of each food. (Generally,
   one serving of a food is the amount of that food that fits in the palm of your hand.

Breakfast			
Food	Element in Food	Food Group	Number of Servings

Lunch			
Food	Element in Food	Food Group	Number of Servings

Dinner			
Food	Element in Food	Food Group	Number of Servings

Name _____ Date _____ Class _____

Properties of p-Block Elements

Use with Chapter 7,
Section 7.2

					Helium 2 **He** 4.003 0
Boron 5 **B** 10.811 3+	Carbon 6 **C** 12.011 2+, 4+, 4−	Nitrogen 7 **N** 14.007 1+, 2+, 3+, 4+, 5+, 1−, 2−, 3−	Oxygen 8 **O** 15.999 2−	Fluorine 9 **F** 18.998 1−	Neon 10 **Ne** 20.180 0
Aluminum 13 **Al** 26.982 3+	Silicon 14 **Si** 28.086 2+, 4+, 4−	Phosphorus 15 **P** 30.974 3+, 5+, 3−	Sulfur 16 **S** 32.065 4+, 6+, 2−	Chlorine 17 **Cl** 35.453 1+, 5+, 7+, 1−	Argon 18 **Ar** 39.948 0
Gallium 31 **Ga** 69.723 3+	Germanium 32 **Ge** 72.64 2+, 4+	Arsenic 33 **As** 74.922 3+, 5+, 3−	Selenium 34 **Se** 78.96 4+, 6+, 2−	Bromine 35 **Br** 79.904 1+, 5+, 1−	Krypton 36 **Kr** 83.80 0
Indium 49 **In** 114.818 3+	Tin 50 **Sn** 118.710 2+, 4+	Antimony 51 **Sb** 121.760 3+, 5+, 3−	Tellurium 52 **Te** 127.60 4+, 6+, 2−	Iodine 53 **I** 126.904 1+, 5+, 7+, 1−	Xenon 54 **Xe** 131.293 0
Thallium 81 **Tl** 204.383 1+, 3+	Lead 82 **Pb** 207.2 2+, 4+	Bismuth 83 **Bi** 208.980 3+, 5+	Polonium 84 **Po** 209 2+, 4+	Astatine 85 **At** 210	Radon 86 **Rn** 222 0

23

Properties of p-Block Elements

**Use with Chapter 7,
Section 7.2**

1. What is the common name for group 7A? Which element in this group is the most reactive? Explain your answer.

_____

_____

2. What are allotropes? Name three p-block elements that have allotropes.

_____

_____

_____

3. What roles do the period-2 elements in groups 4A–7A play in the chemistry of living organisms?

_____

_____

_____

4. Explain why the noble gases are relatively unreactive.

_____

_____

5. Sulfur and fluorine combine to form the compound SF_6. What other elements might form a similar compound with fluorine? Explain why.

_____

_____

6. Oxides are compounds in which oxygen is combined with another element. Use the table to identify differences between the oxides of metals and nonmetals.

Oxide	Physical State at Room Temperature	Reaction
Aluminum oxide	Solid	Reacts with nitric acid to form aluminum nitrate
Sulfur dioxide	Gas	Reacts with water to give sulfuric and sulfurous acid
Carbon dioxide	Gas	Reacts with water to give carbonic acid
Magnesium oxide	Solid	Reacts with sulfuric acid to form magnesium sulfate

_____

_____

_____

Name _____ Date _____ Class _____

Transition Metals

Use with Chapter 7,
Section 7.3

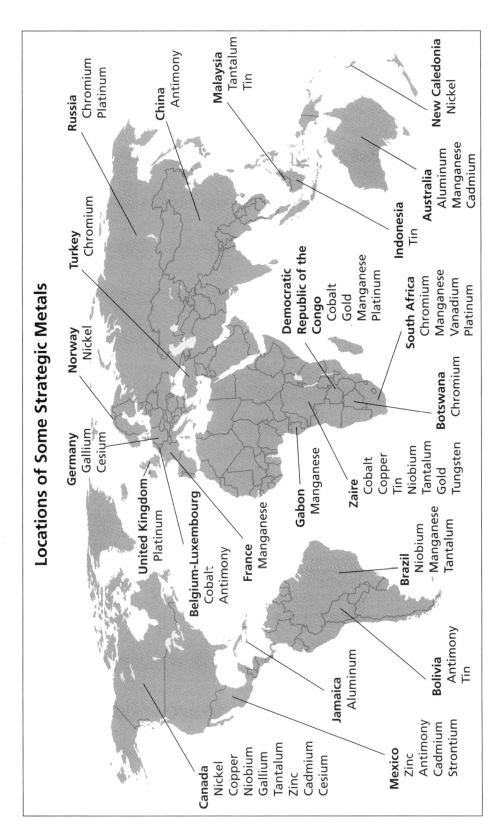

Locations of Some Strategic Metals

Russia
Chromium
Platinum

China
Antimony

Malaysia
Tantalum
Tin

New Caledonia
Nickel

Turkey
Chromium

Norway
Nickel

Indonesia
Tin

Australia
Aluminum
Manganese
Cadmium

**Democratic
Republic of the
Congo**
Cobalt
Gold
Manganese
Platinum

South Africa
Chromium
Manganese
Vanadium
Platinum

Botswana
Chromium

Germany
Gallium
Cesium

United Kingdom
Platinum

Belgium-Luxembourg
Cobalt
Antimony

France
Manganese

Gabon
Manganese

Zaire
Cobalt
Copper
Tin
Niobium
Tantalum
Gold
Tungsten

Brazil
Niobium
Manganese
Tantalum

Jamaica
Aluminum

Bolivia
Antimony
Tin

Mexico
Zinc
Antimony
Cadmium
Strontium

Canada
Nickel
Copper
Niobium
Gallium
Tantalum
Zinc
Cadmium
Cesium

TEACHING TRANSPARENCY WORKSHEET 24

Transition Metals

**Use with Chapter 7,
Section 7.3**

1. Of the metals listed on the map, how many are transition metals? List the transition metals.

_____

_____

_____

2. The United States imports most of the chromium it uses to make products such as stainless steel. Name three countries with chromium deposits.

_____

3. The United States imports most of the manganese it needs. Manganese is a component of the hard steel used for heavy machinery. On which continents are there large deposits of manganese?

_____

4. The human body requires trace amounts of a number of transition metals. Which of these transition metals are listed on the map?

_____

_____

5. Which metal—vanadium, chromium, or manganese—has the highest melting point? Why?

_____

_____

6. What use do the metals found in the United Kingdom and New Caledonia have in common?

_____

_____

7. Explain why the nickel and copper ores mined in Canada are brightly colored. How can color be used to detect the charge on a transition metal ion?

_____

_____

_____

8. What property does the cobalt mined in Belgium have in common with the nickel mined in Norway?

_____

TEACHING TRANSPARENCY MASTER **25**

Formation of Ions

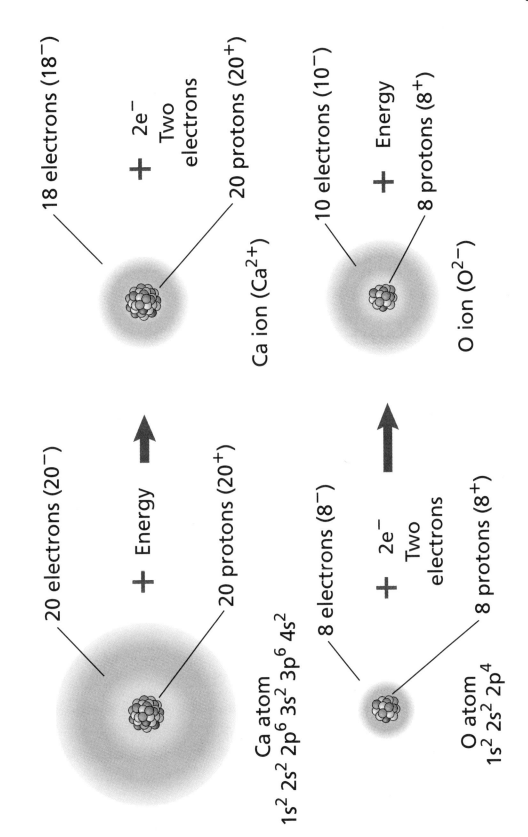

18 electrons (18⁻)

$+$ 2e⁻ Two electrons

20 protons (20⁺)

Ca ion (Ca^{2+})

10 electrons (10⁻)

$+$ Energy

8 protons (8⁺)

O ion (O^{2-})

20 electrons (20⁻)

$+$ Energy

20 protons (20⁺)

Ca atom
$1s^2\ 2s^2\ 2p^6\ 3s^2\ 3p^6\ 4s^2$

8 electrons (8⁻)

$+$ 2e⁻ Two electrons

8 protons (8⁺)

O atom
$1s^2\ 2s^2\ 2p^4$

Name ______________________ Date ______________ Class ______________

TEACHING TRANSPARENCY WORKSHEET 25

Formation of Ions

Use with Chapter 8, Section 8.1

1. What are the names of the two elements shown?

____

2. Are the elements shown on the left sides of the two equations neutral? How can you tell?

____

3. What is the name for the energy needed to remove electrons from an atom, such as the Ca atom shown?

____

4. What kind of charge does the Ca atom take on as a result of the reaction? What is the name for an ion with that kind of charge?

____

5. What kind of charge does the O atom take on as a result of the reaction? What is the name for an ion with that kind of charge?

____

6. Is the outer electron configuration of the Ca atom before the reaction a very stable one? How can you tell?

____

7. Is the outer electron configuration of the O atom before the reaction a very stable one? How can you tell?

____

8. Is the outer electron configuration of the Ca ion after the reaction a very stable one? How can you tell?

____

9. Is the outer electron configuration of the O ion after the reaction a very stable one? How can you tell?

____

10. What is the electron configuration of the Ca ion? What neutral atom has the same configuration, and in what chemical family is it located in the periodic table?

____

11. What is the electron configuration of the O ion? What neutral atom has the same configuration, and in what chemical family is it located in the periodic table?

____

TEACHING TRANSPARENCY MASTER (26)

Ionic Bonds

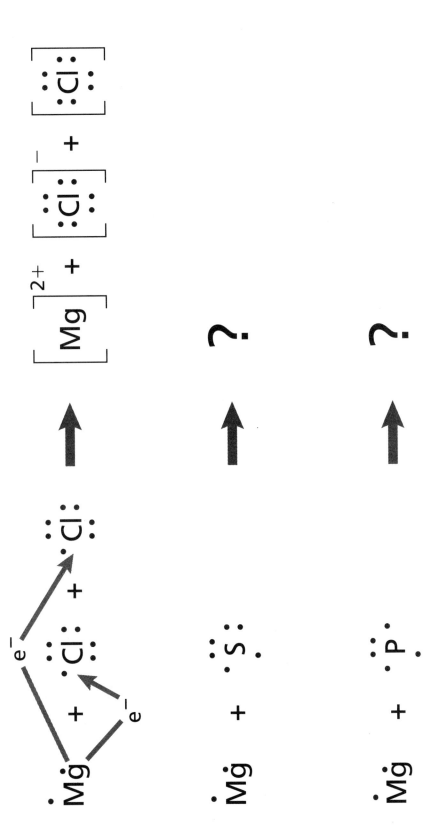

TEACHING TRANSPARENCY WORKSHEET 26

Ionic Bonds

**Use with Chapter 8,
Section 8.2**

1. How many valence electrons does a neutral magnesium (Mg) atom have? _____

2. What is the charge on a magnesium ion? What does magnesium have to do to form such an ion, and why does it tend to do so?

_____

_____

3. How many valence electrons does a single neutral chlorine (Cl) atom have? _____

4. What is the charge on a chloride ion? What does chlorine have to do to form such an ion, and why does it tend to do so?

_____

_____

5. How many magnesium atoms and how many chlorine atoms react to form one formula unit of magnesium chloride? Why? What is the formula of magnesium chloride?

_____

_____

6. What kind of compound is magnesium chloride? What happens to electrons during the formation of the compound? What holds the atoms together in the compound?

_____

_____

_____

7. What is the formula of the ionic compound formed by magnesium and sulfur (S) atoms? Explain why, in terms of electron transfer, stability, and overall charge.

_____

_____

_____

_____

8. What is the formula of the ionic compound formed by magnesium and phosphorus (P) atoms? Explain why, in terms of electron transfer, stability, and overall charge.

_____

_____

_____

_____

Formulas for Ionic Compounds

**Use with Chapter 8,
Section 8.3**

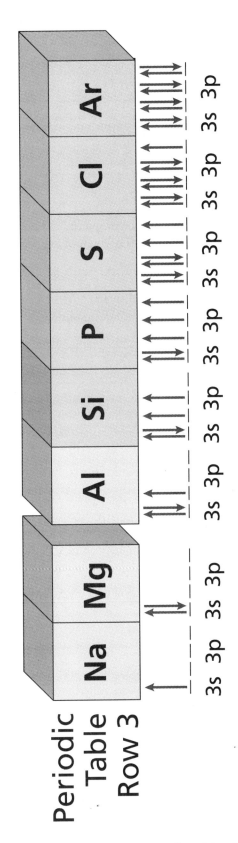

Periodic
Table
Row 3

Formulas for Ionic Compounds

**Use with Chapter 8,
Section 8.3**

1. How many valence electrons are there in an atom of sodium (Na)? What would a sodium atom tend to do in bonding with another atom to form an ionic compound? Why?

_____

_____

2. How many valence electrons are there in an atom of phosphorus (P)? What would a phosphorus atom tend to do in bonding with another atom to form an ionic compound? Why?

_____

_____

3. What would be the formula and name of the ionic compound formed when sodium reacts with phosphorus? What are the oxidation numbers of each of the ions present?

_____

4. How many valence electrons are in an atom of sulfur (S)? What would a sulfur atom tend to do in bonding with another atom to form an ionic compound? Why?

_____

_____

5. What would be the formula and name of the ionic compound formed when sodium reacts with sulfur? What are the oxidation numbers of each of the ions present?

_____

6. How many valence electrons are in an atom of aluminum (Al)? What would an aluminum atom tend to do in bonding with another atom to form an ionic compound? Why?

_____

_____

7. How many valence electrons are in an atom of chlorine (Cl)? What would a chlorine atom tend to do in bonding with another atom to form an ionic compound? Why?

_____

_____

8. What would be the formula and name of the ionic compound formed when aluminum reacts with chlorine? What are the oxidation numbers of each of the ions present?

_____

9. What would be the formula and name of the ionic compound formed when aluminum reacts with sulfur? What are the oxidation numbers of each of the ions present?

_____

TEACHING TRANSPARENCY MASTER

28

Metallic Bonding

**Use with Chapter 8,
Section 8.4**

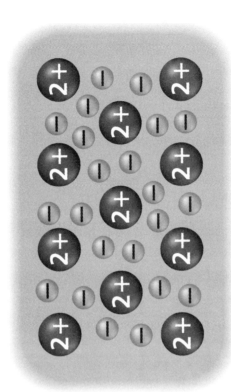

Group 2A Metal Atoms

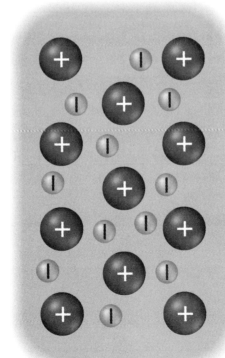

Group 1A Metal Atoms

TEACHING TRANSPARENCY WORKSHEET (28)

Metallic Bonding

**Use with Chapter 8,
Section 8.4**

1. What is a regular, repeating three-dimensional arrangement of atoms called?

_____

2. Do the separate electrons that are shown belong exclusively to a single atom? What word is used to describe such electrons?

_____

3. Are the electrons shown the only ones actually present? Explain.

_____

4. Why are the central atoms shown as positively charged?

_____

_____

5. How does the number of separate electrons shown for the group 1A metal atoms compare to the number of atoms? Explain why in terms of valence electrons.

_____

_____

6. How does the number of separate electrons shown for the group 2A metal atoms compare to the number of atoms?

_____

7. What holds the metal atoms together in such an arrangement?

_____

_____

8. What term is used to describe this model of metallic bonding? _____

9. How well do metals tend to conduct electricity? How does the model of metallic bonding account for that property?

_____

_____

_____

10. Do metals tend to be brittle, or are they malleable and ductile? How does the model of metallic bonding account for that property?

_____

_____

_____

TEACHING TRANSPARENCY MASTER   (29)

Lewis Structures

Use with Chapter 9,
Section 9.3

Formula	Step 1	Step 2	Step 3	Step 4	Step 5	Step 6
N_2H_4	H N N H H H	14	7	H—N—N—H H H	H—N—N—H (with lone pairs) H H 2	Unnecessary (octets complete)
SiO_2	O Si O			O—Si—O		

TEACHING TRANSPARENCY WORKSHEET (29)

Lewis Structures

Use with Chapter 9,
Section 9.3

1. Step 1 in drawing the Lewis structure for a molecule is to decide which atoms of the molecule are most likely the terminal ones. In the transparency, why are the hydrogen (H) atoms in hydrazine (N_2H_4) shown as the terminal atoms?

_____

2. Step 2 in drawing a Lewis structure involves determining the total number of valence electrons in the atoms in the molecule. Explain why the total number of valence electrons in N_2H_4 is 14.

_____

_____

3. Step 3 in drawing a Lewis structure requires finding the number of bonding pairs. What must be done to the result of step 2 to find the number of bonding pairs? Verify that this is so in the case of N_2H_4 in the transparency.

_____

_____

4. In step 4 in the transparency, one bonding pair has been placed between each pair of bonded atoms in N_2H_4. How many such bonding pairs are shown in step 4, and what symbol is used to represent them?

_____

5. Step 5 requires subtraction of the number of bonding pairs used in step 4 from the number of bonding pairs determined in step 3. Verify that the result is 2 for N_2H_4. Lone pairs are then placed around each terminal atom to achieve a full outer level, and any remaining pairs are assigned to the central atom(s). Explain the drawing that has resulted for N_2H_4.

_____

_____

6. In step 6, if any central atom drawn in step 5 does not have an octet, lone pairs from the terminal atoms must be converted to double or triple bonds involving the central atom. Why was this extra step unnecessary in the case of N_2H_4?

_____

_____

7. What number should be placed in the blank for step 2 for the silicon dioxide (SiO_2) molecule?

_____

8. What number should be placed in the blank for step 3 for SiO_2?

_____

Name _____ Date _____ Class _____

VSEPR Model and Molecular Shape

VSEPR Model and Molecular Shape

Use with Chapter 9,
Section 9.4

1. The shapes of the molecules shown have been determined by means of the VSEPR model. What is the basic assumption of this model?

_____

_____

2. How many lone pairs and how many shared pairs of electrons surround the boron (B) atom in the borane (BH_3) molecule shown?

_____

3. What is the shape of the BH_3 molecule? Explain why.

_____

_____

_____

4. How many lone pairs and how many shared pairs of electrons surround the carbon (C) atom in the methane (CH_4) molecule shown? What is the shape of the molecule?

_____

5. How many lone pairs and how many shared pairs of electrons surround the nitrogen (N) atom in the ammonia (NH_3) molecule shown? What is the shape of the molecule?

_____

6. How many lone pairs and how many shared pairs of electrons surround the oxygen (O) atom in the water (H_2O) molecule shown? What is the shape of the molecule?

_____

7. How many lone pairs and how many shared pairs of electrons surround the fluorine (F) atom in the hydrogen fluoride (HF) molecule shown? What is the shape of the molecule?

_____

Electronegativity and Polarity

**Use with Chapter 9,
Section 9.5**

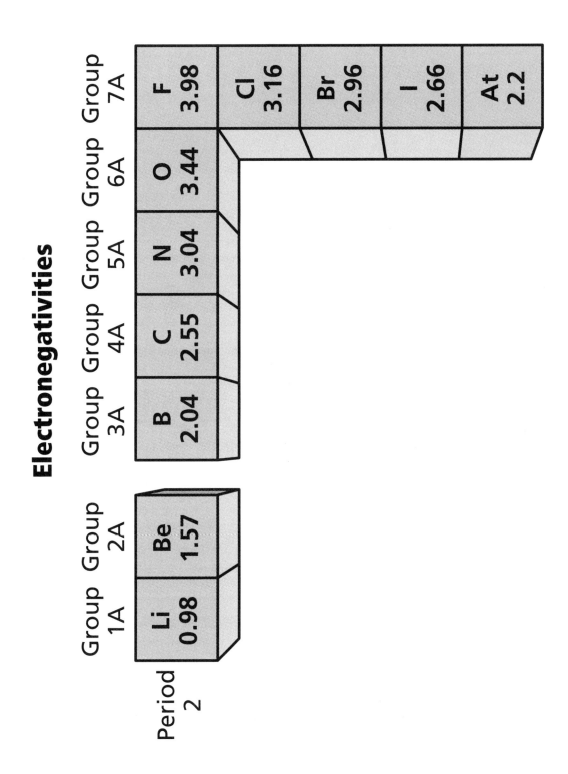

Name _____ Date _____ Class _____

Electronegativity and Polarity

**Use with Chapter 9,
Section 9.5**

1. What is electronegativity?

_____

2. The electronegativities of the elements of period 2 and of group 17 of the periodic table are
shown. What trends in electronegativity do you see across the period? Down the group?

_____

_____

3. When there is an electronegativity difference between two covalently bonded atoms,
what is true of the bond between them? Toward which of the atoms are the shared
electrons more attracted?

_____

4. What kind of bond exists between a carbon (C) atom and a chlorine (Cl) atom? (Assume
that a bond is nonpolar covalent if the electronegativity difference is 0, polar covalent if
the difference is greater than 0 but not more than 1.70, and ionic if the difference is more
than 1.70.)

_____

5. Given your answer to question 4 and your knowledge of molecular shapes, is a carbon
tetrachloride (CCl_4) molecule polar or nonpolar? Explain.

_____

_____

6. What kind of bond exists between a nitrogen (N) atom and a fluorine (F) atom? Is a
nitrogen trifluoride (NF_3) molecule polar or nonpolar? Explain.

_____

_____

7. What kind of bond exists between a beryllium (Be) atom and a bromine (Br) atom? Is a
beryllium bromide ($BeBr_2$) molecule polar or nonpolar? Explain.

_____

_____

8. What kind of bond exists between a beryllium (Be) atom and a fluorine (F) atom?

_____

9. What kind of bond exists between a boron (B) atom and an iodine (I) atom? Is a boron
triiodide (BI_3) molecule polar or nonpolar? Explain.

_____

_____

TEACHING TRANSPARENCY MASTER **32**

Parts of a Balanced Chemical Equation

Use with Chapter 10,
Section 10.1

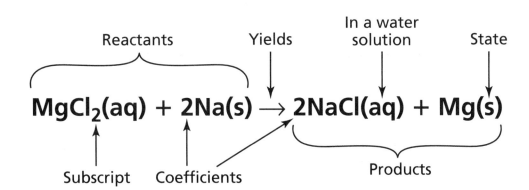

$$MgCl_2(aq) + 2Na(s) \rightarrow 2NaCl(aq) + Mg(s)$$

Reactants — Yields — In a water solution — State

Subscript — Coefficients — Products

Equation 1:

$$2KI(aq) + Pb(NO_3)_2(aq) \rightarrow PbI_2(s) + 2KNO_3(aq)$$

Equation 2:

$$6HCl(aq) + 2Al(s) \rightarrow 2AlCl_3(Aq) + 3H_2(g)$$

TEACHING TRANSPARENCY WORKSHEET   **32**

Parts of a Balanced Chemical Equation

Use with Chapter 10, Section 10.1

Examine the parts of the chemical equation at the top of the transparency. Use this information to answer the following questions about Equation 1 and Equation 2.

1. Write Equation 1 as a sentence.

_____

_____

_____

2. Write Equation 2 as a sentence.

_____

_____

_____

3. What substances are reactants in

  a. Equation 1? _____   **b.** Equation 2? _____

4. What substances are products in

  a. Equation 1? _____   **b.** Equation 2? _____

5. List the coefficients used in

  a. Equation 1. _____   **b.** Equation 2. _____

6. What substances are in aqueous solution in

  a. Equation 1? _____   **b.** Equation 2? _____

7. What substance shown is a gas? _____

8. What is the state of PbI_2 in Equation 1? _____

9. What state is not represented in either equation? _____

10. What do the subscripts tell you in the formulas for

  a. $AlCl_3$? _____

  b. KNO_3? _____

  c. $Pb(NO_3)_2$? _____

_____

TEACHING TRANSPARENCY MASTER   **33**

Balancing Chemical Equations

Use with Chapter 10,
Section 10.1

Steps for Balancing Equations

1. Write the skeleton equation for the reaction.

2. Count the atoms of each element in the reactants.

3. Count the atoms of each element in the products.

4. Change the coefficients to make the number of atoms of each element equal on each side of the equation.

5. Write the coefficients in the lowest possible ratio.

6. Check your work.

Balancing Chemical Equations

Use with Chapter 10, Section 10.1

1. Examine the following equation.

$$Mg(s) + Ag_2S(s) \rightarrow MgS(s) + Ag(s)$$

   a. How many atoms of magnesium are on each side of the equation? _____

   b. Which element does not have the same number of atoms on both sides of the equation?

   _____

   c. Write the balanced equation for this reaction. _____

2. Follow the steps for balancing a chemical equation and write a response for each step for the reaction in which iron metal (Fe) burns in oxygen (O_2) to form iron(III) oxide (Fe_2O_3).

   Step 1: _____

   Step 2: _____

   Step 3: _____

   Step 4: _____

   Step 5: _____

   Step 6: _____

3. For each of the following, use at least one of the rules for balancing equations to explain why the equation is not properly balanced. Then write a correctly balanced equation for each reaction.

   a. $2H_2O(l) + 2CO_2(g) \rightarrow 2H_2CO_3(aq)$

   _____

   _____

   b. $MgNO_{32}(aq) + 2K(s) \rightarrow Mg(s) + 2KNO_3(aq)$

   _____

   _____

   c. $AlCl_3(aq) + AgNO_3(aq) \rightarrow AgCl(s) + Al(NO_3)_3(aq)$

   _____

   _____

TEACHING TRANSPARENCY MASTER (34)

The Activity Series

Use with Chapter 10, Section 10.2

Activity Series of Metals	
Metal	**Reactions**
Lithium Rubidium Potassium Calcium Sodium	All replace the hydrogen in water and acids. Each replaces metals listed below it.
Magnesium Aluminum Manganese Zinc Iron Nickel Tin Lead	All replace the hydrogen in acids. Each replaces metals listed below it.
Copper Silver Platinum Gold	All are mostly unreactive as far as replacing other metals in a compound.

Activity Series of Halogens	
Halogen	**Reactions**
Fluorine Chlorine Bromine Iodine	Each replaces halogens listed below it.

The Activity Series

**Use with Chapter 10,
Section 10.2**

1. For each of the following pairs of elements, underline the one that would replace the other element in a compound.

   a. calcium, tin

   b. bromine, fluorine

   c. aluminum, potassium

   d. zinc, sodium

   e. iron, copper

   f. iodine, chlorine

   g. silver, lead

2. For each of the following reactants, use the activity series to determine whether the reaction would take place or not. If no reaction takes place, write *NR* in the blank. If a reaction does take place, write the formulas for the products of the reaction. (Hint: If an active metal replaces the hydrogen in water, the hydroxide of the active metal forms.)

   a. $Li(s) + Fe(NO_3)_3(aq) \rightarrow$ _____

   b. $Au(s) + HCl(aq) \rightarrow$ _____

   c. $Cl_2(g) + KBr(aq) \rightarrow$ _____

   d. $Cu(s) + Al(NO_3)_3(aq) \rightarrow$ _____

   e. $Ag(s) + HBr(aq) \rightarrow$ _____

   f. $Ni(s) + SnCl_2(aq) \rightarrow$ _____

3. Magnesium metal can be used to remove tarnish from silver items. Silver tarnish is the corrosion that occurs when silver metal reacts with substances in the environment, especially those containing sulfur. Why would magnesium remove tarnish from silver?

   _____

   _____

4. Use the activity series for metals to explain why copper metal is used in plumbing where the water might contain compounds of many different metals.

   _____

   _____

5. The last four metals in the activity series of metals are commonly referred to as the "coinage metals." Why would these metals be chosen over more active metals for use in coins? Why do you think some more active metals, such as zinc or nickel, are sometimes used in coins?

   _____

   _____

   _____

35

Summary of Reaction Types

**Use with Chapter 10,
Section 10.2**

Predicting Products of Chemical Reactions		
Class of reaction	**Reactants**	**Probable products**
Synthesis	Two or more substances	One compound
Combustion	A metal and oxygen	The oxide of the metal
	A nonmetal and oxygen	The oxide of the nonmetal
	A compound and oxygen	Two or more oxides
Decomposition	One compound	Two or more elements and/or compounds
Single-replacement	A metal and a compound	A new compound and the replaced metal
	A nonmetal and a compound	A new compound and the replaced nonmetal
Double-replacement	Two compounds	Two different compounds, one of which is often a solid, water, or a gas

Summary of Reaction Types

Use with Chapter 10,
Section 10.2

1. For each set of reactants listed below, identify the type of reaction that the reactants might undergo. List as many reaction types as may apply. Assume that all the reactants for the reaction are listed.

   a. a compound and an element _____

   b. two compounds _____

   c. one compound _____

2. For each set of reaction products listed below, identify the type of reaction that might have formed the products. List as many reaction types as may apply. Assume that all the products for the reaction are listed.

   a. a compound and an element _____

   b. two compounds _____

   c. one compound _____

3. Classify each of the following examples according to the type of reaction involved. List as many reaction types as may apply.

   a. A match burns.

   _____

   b. The carbonic acid found in soft drinks breaks down into bubbles of carbon dioxide and water.

   _____

   c. Phosphorous and oxygen react rapidly, forming diphosphorous pentoxide.

   _____

   d. An iron nail is placed into a copper sulfate solution. Copper metal appears on the nail.

   _____

   e. The acid in baking powder reacts with baking soda ($NaHCO_3$), forming carbon dioxide gas and other products.

   _____

   f. Water and sulfur trioxide react to form sulfuric acid.

   _____

   g. Copper wire is placed in a silver nitrate solution. The solution turns blue, which is the color of the copper ion, and solid silver forms on the wire.

   _____

Name ____________________ Date ____________ Class ____________

TEACHING TRANSPARENCY MASTER **36**

Types of Equations

Use with Chapter 10, Section 10.3

Complete equation:

$$2KOH(aq) + H_2SO_4(aq) \rightarrow K_2SO_4(aq) + 2H_2O(l)$$

Complete ionic equation:

$$2K^+(aq) + 2OH^-(aq) + 2H^+(aq) + SO_4^{2-}(aq) \rightarrow 2K^+(aq) + SO_4^{2-}(aq) + 2H_2O(l)$$

Net ionic equation:

$$OH^-(aq) + H^+(aq) \rightarrow H_2O(l)$$

TEACHING TRANSPARENCY WORKSHEET **36**

Types of Equations

Use with Chapter 10, Section 10.3

1. Write the complete equation as a sentence.

_____

_____

_____

2. What is a spectator ion?

_____

3. What are the spectator ions in this reaction?

_____

4. Compare and contrast each pair below.

    a. complete equations, complete ionic equations

_____

_____

    b. complete ionic equations, net ionic equations

_____

_____

_____

5. For the reaction between aqueous silver nitrate and aqueous sodium chloride, write each of the following. The products of the reaction are aqueous sodium nitrate and solid silver chloride.

    a. complete equation

_____

    b. complete ionic equation

_____

    c. net ionic equation

_____

6. What is the net ionic equation for the reaction between aqueous calcium hydroxide and nitric acid? The products of this reaction are aqueous calcium nitrate and water. How does this net ionic equation compare to the net ionic equation shown on the transparency?

_____

Name _____ Date _____ Class _____

Mass-to-Mole and Mole-to-Particles Conversions for Compounds

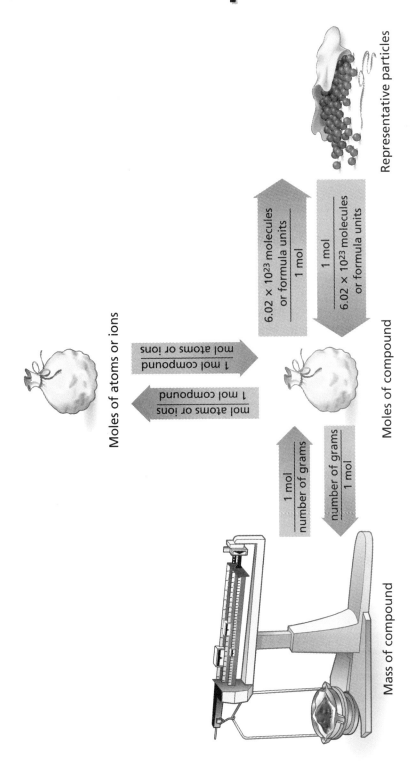

Representative particles

$\dfrac{6.02 \times 10^{23} \text{ molecules or formula units}}{1 \text{ mol}}$

$\dfrac{1 \text{ mol}}{6.02 \times 10^{23} \text{ molecules or formula units}}$

Moles of atoms or ions

$\dfrac{1 \text{ mol compound}}{\text{mol atoms or ions}}$

$\dfrac{\text{mol atoms or ions}}{1 \text{ mol compound}}$

Moles of compound

$\dfrac{1 \text{ mol}}{\text{number of grams}}$

$\dfrac{\text{number of grams}}{1 \text{ mol}}$

Mass of compound

TEACHING TRANSPARENCY WORKSHEET (37)

Mass-to-Mole and Mole-to-Particles Conversions for Compounds

Use with Chapter 11, Section 11.3

1. According to the diagram, what *three* quantities can you calculate if you know the number of moles of a compound?

   _____

   _____

2. According to the diagram, what *three* quantities can you calculate from a mass measurement of a compound?

   _____

   _____

3. If you were given the number of moles of a compound, what quantity would you need to know to calculate the mass of that number of moles of the compound?

   _____

4. If you were given the number of moles of a compound, what information would you need to know to determine each of the conversion factors necessary to find the number of moles of each atom or ion in the compound?

   _____

5. You are given a 2.0-mol sample of calcium carbonate ($CaCO_3$). The molar mass of $CaCO_3$ is 100.09 g/mol. Write the conversion factor you would use to determine correctly each of the following quantities.

   a. the mass in grams of the sample

   _____

   b. the number of formula units of $CaCO_3$ in the sample

   _____

   c. the number of moles of oxygen atoms in the sample

   _____

6. Write the conversion factors in the order you would use them to determine correctly each of the following quantities in a sample of 2.0×10^{24} molecules of ethane (C_2H_6). The molar mass of ethane is 30.08 g/mol.

   a. the mass in grams of the sample

   _____

   b. the number of carbon atoms in the sample

   _____

Mass-to-Mass Conversions

**Use with Chapter 12,
Section 12.2**

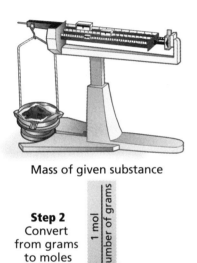

Mass of given substance

Step 1
Start with a
balanced equation

Mass of unknown substance

no direct conversion

Step 2
Convert
from grams
to moles

$$\frac{1\ mol}{number\ of\ grams}$$

Step 4
Convert
from moles
to grams

$$\frac{number\ of\ grams}{1\ mol}$$

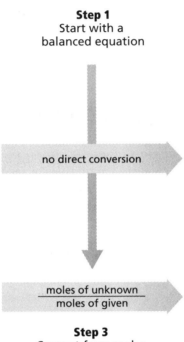

Mole of given substance

$$\frac{moles\ of\ unknown}{moles\ of\ given}$$

Step 3
Convert from moles
of given to moles of
unknown

Moles of unknown substance

TEACHING TRANSPARENCY WORKSHEET (38)

Mass-to-Mass Conversions

Use with Chapter 12, Section 12.2

1. What conversion factor would you use to convert correctly from the mass of a given substance to the number of moles of the given substance?

   _____

2. What conversion factor would you use to convert correctly from the number of moles of a given substance to the number of moles of an unknown substance?

   _____

3. What conversion factor would you use to convert correctly from the number of moles of the unknown substance to the mass of the unknown substance?

   _____

4. What is the name of the conversion factor in question 2?

   _____

5. What do you need to know to find the conversion factor in question 2?

   _____

Use the following balanced chemical equation and table to answer questions 6.

$$2N_2(g) + O_2(g) \rightarrow 2N_2O(g)$$

Compound	Molar Mass (g/mol)
N_2	28.02
O_2	32.00
N_2O	44.02

6. Write the conversion factors in the order you would use them to determine correctly each of the following.

   a. the number of moles of N_2O produced when 26.5 g N_2 reacts with excess oxygen

   _____

   b. the mass of N_2 needed to produce 11.5 g N_2O

   _____

   c. the mass of N_2 needed to react completely with 1.56 g O_2

   _____

   d. the mass of N_2O produced when 7.05 g O_2 reacts with excess nitrogen

   _____

Limiting Reactants

**Use with Chapter 12,
Section 12.3**

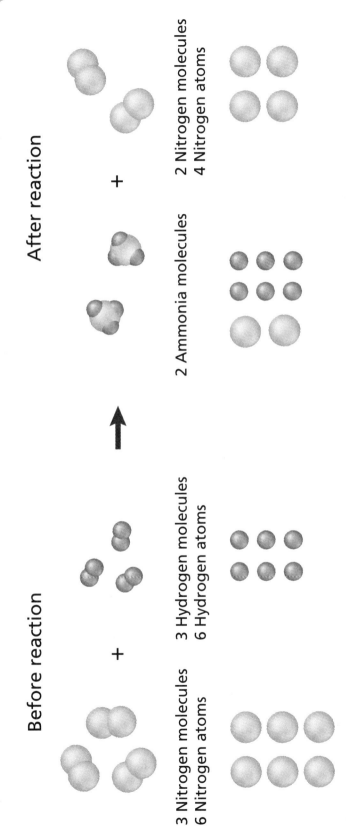

Before reaction

After reaction

+

+

3 Nitrogen molecules
6 Nitrogen atoms

3 Hydrogen molecules
6 Hydrogen atoms

2 Ammonia molecules

2 Nitrogen molecules
4 Nitrogen atoms

TEACHING TRANSPARENCY WORKSHEET **39**

Limiting Reactants

**Use with Chapter 12,
Section 12.3**

1. How many N_2 molecules are shown in the transparency? N atoms?

_____

2. How many H_2 molecules are shown? H atoms?

_____

3. What is the ratio of H atoms to N atoms in one NH_3 molecule?

_____

4. How many H atoms would be needed to react with all the N atoms shown in the transparency?

_____

5. How many N atoms would be needed to react with all the H atoms shown in the transparency?

_____

6. According to your answers to questions 4 and 5, how many N_2 molecules and H_2 molecules will be used up completely by the reaction shown in the transparency?

_____

7. Which reactant will remain after the reaction? How many molecules?

_____

8. Complete the diagram below by drawing the products of the chemical reaction in the box.

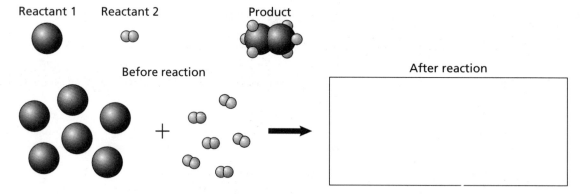

9. Which reactant in the diagram is the limiting reactant?

_____

10. Which reactant in the diagram is in excess?

_____

TEACHING TRANSPARENCY MASTER 40

Manometer

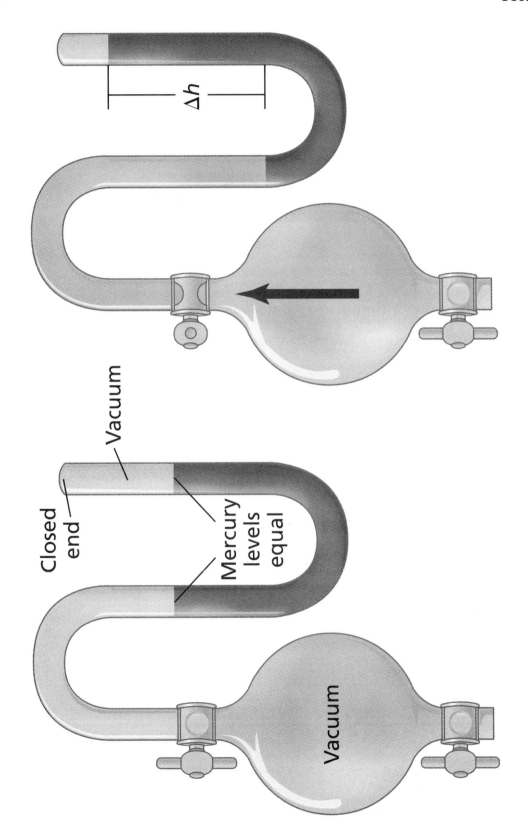

Δh

Vacuum

Closed end

Mercury levels equal

Vacuum

Manometer

1. The transparency shows a manometer. Briefly describe its parts.

_____

_____

_____

2. Why are the levels of the mercury in the two arms of the U-tube the same when there is no gas in the flask?

_____

_____

3. What happens when gas enters the flask?

_____

_____

_____

4. Compare the force exerted by the gas to the force exerted by the mercury contained in the portion of the closed-end arm labeled Δh.

_____

5. If the flask was filled with air at a pressure of 1.00 atm, what would be the value of Δh in millimeters of Hg?

_____

6. If the flask was filled with air at a pressure of 0.50 atm, what would be the value of Δh in millimeters of Hg?

_____

7. A sample of gas is collected in the flask. The value of Δh is 76.0 mm Hg. What is the pressure of the gas in mm Hg? In atm?

_____

_____

8. How does the vapor pressure of mercury affect the pressure reading of the manometer?

_____

_____

Name _____ Date _____ Class _____

Phase Diagrams

**Use with Chapter 13,
Section 13.4**

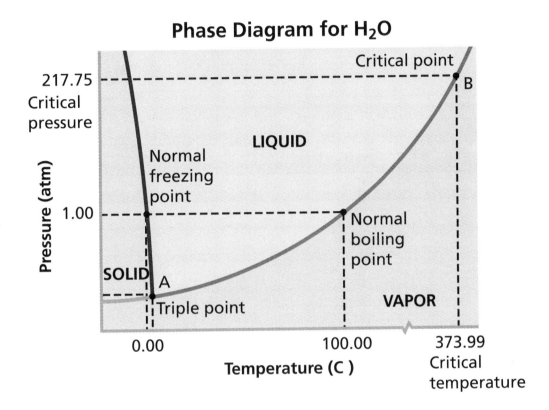

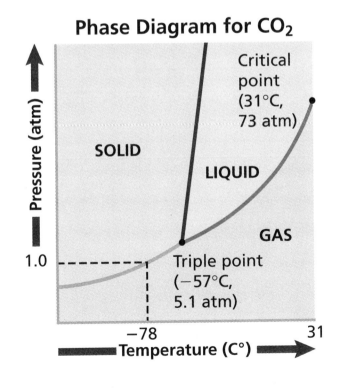

TEACHING TRANSPARENCY WORKSHEET **41**

Phase Diagrams

**Use with Chapter 13,
Section 13.4**

1. What variables are plotted on a phase diagram?

_____

2. How many phases of water are represented in its phase diagram? What are they?

_____

3. Use the phase diagram for water to complete the following table.

Temperature (°C)	Pressure (atm)	Phase
200	1	
−2	1	
150	100	
−2	0.001	
30	0.8	
	1	liquid
100.00		vapor

4. What phases of water coexist at each point along the red curve?

_____

5. What two phase changes occur at each point along the yellow curve in the phase diagram
for water?

_____

6. Look at the phase diagram for carbon dioxide. Above which pressure and temperature is
carbon dioxide unable to exist as a liquid?

_____

7. At which pressure and temperature do the solid, liquid, and gaseous phases of carbon
dioxide coexist?

_____

Pressure vs. Volume Graph

**Use with Chapter 14,
Section 14.1**

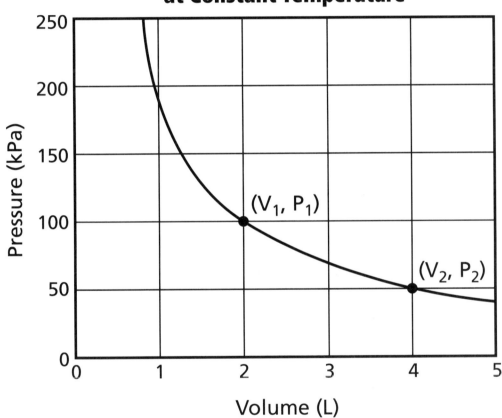

**Pressure vs. Volume for a Gas
at Constant Temperature**

TEACHING TRANSPARENCY WORKSHEET **42**

Pressure vs. Volume Graph

**Use with Chapter 14,
Section 14.1**

1. Based on this graph, how is the volume of a gas affected by increased pressure at constant temperature?

_____

_____

2. The relationship between the volume and pressure of a gas at constant temperature is an inversely proportional relationship. Based on the evidence in this graph, define the inversely proportional relationship.

_____

_____

3. What do you notice when you multiply the pressure by the volume for any point on the line on the graph?

_____

_____

_____

_____

_____

4. Based on the mathematical relationship derived from this graph, what is the pressure of the gas at 3.00 L at constant temperature?

_____

5. What gas law does this graph represent?

_____

6. What mathematical expression is used to define this law? Define all symbols used.

_____

_____

_____

7. A sample of gas is compressed from 3.25 L to 1.20 L at constant temperature. If the pressure of this gas in the 3.25-L volume is 100.00 kPa, what will the pressure be at 1.20 L? List all known and unknown variables. Show all your work.

_____

_____

_____

_____

Volume vs. Temperature Graph

**Use with Chapter 14,
Section 14.1**

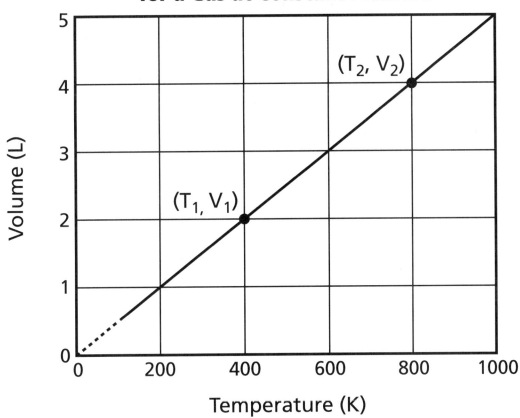

**Volume vs. Kelvin Temperature
for a Gas at Constant Pressure**

(T_2, V_2)

(T_1, V_1)

Volume (L)

Temperature (K)

TEACHING TRANSPARENCY WORKSHEET

Volume vs. Temperature Graph

**Use with Chapter 14,
Section 14.1**

1. Notice that this graph shows kelvin temperatures. How are the kelvin scale and Celsius scale related mathematically?

   _____

   _____

2. Based on this graph, how is the volume of a gas affected by increased temperature at constant pressure?

   _____

   _____

3. The relationship between the volume and temperature of a gas at constant pressure is a directly proportional relationship. Based on the evidence in this graph, define the directly proportional relationship.

   _____

   _____

4. What do you notice when you divide the temperature by the volume for any point on the line on the graph?

   _____

   _____

   _____

   _____

5. What law does this graph represent?

   _____

6. What mathematical expression is used to define this law? Define all symbols used.

   _____

   _____

   _____

7. The kelvin temperature of a sample of gas is decreased from 460 K to 240 K at constant pressure. If the volume of this gas at 460 K is 2.50 L, what will the volume be at 240 K? List all known and unknown variables. Show all your work.

   _____

   _____

   _____

Burning of Methane Gas

**Use with Chapter 14,
Section 14.4**

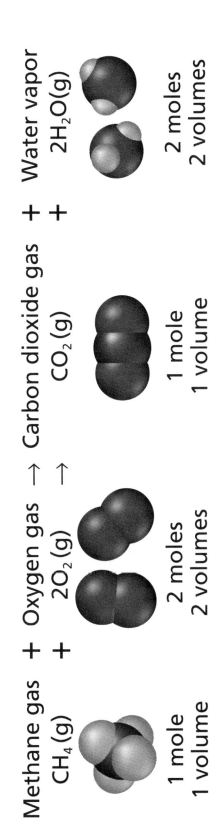

Methane gas + Oxygen gas → Carbon dioxide gas + Water vapor
CH_4 (g) + $2O_2$ (g) → CO_2 (g) + $2H_2O$(g)

1 mole   2 moles   1 mole   2 moles
1 volume   2 volumes   1 volume   2 volumes

TEACHING TRANSPARENCY WORKSHEET 44

Burning of Methane Gas

Use with Chapter 14,
Section 14.4

1. What do the coefficients in chemical equations involving gases, solids, and liquids represent?

   _____

2. What does Avogadro's principle state?

   _____

3. Based on Avogadro's principle, the coefficients in chemical equations involving only gases represent two types of quantities. Name the two quantities.

   _____

   _____

4. Based on the balanced equation for the complete combustion of methane, how many liters of carbon dioxide, $CO_2(g)$, and water vapor, $H_2O(g)$, are produced by the complete combustion of 1 L of methane gas, CH_4?

   _____

   _____

5. What volume of oxygen gas is needed for the complete combustion of 8.00 L of methane gas, CH_4? Assume that the pressure and temperature of the reactants are the same. Show all your work.

   _____

   _____

   _____

   _____

6. Write a balanced equation for the complete combustion of propane gas, C_3H_8, with oxygen, O_2, to form carbon dioxide, CO_2, and water, H_2O.

   _____

7. What volume of carbon dioxide gas, CO_2, is produced when 7.00 L of propane gas, C_3H_8, undergoes complete combustion, as shown in your answer to question 6? Show all your work.

   _____

   _____

   _____

   _____

Solubility–Temperature Graphs

Use with Chapter 15, Section 15.1

Solubilities as a Function of Temperature

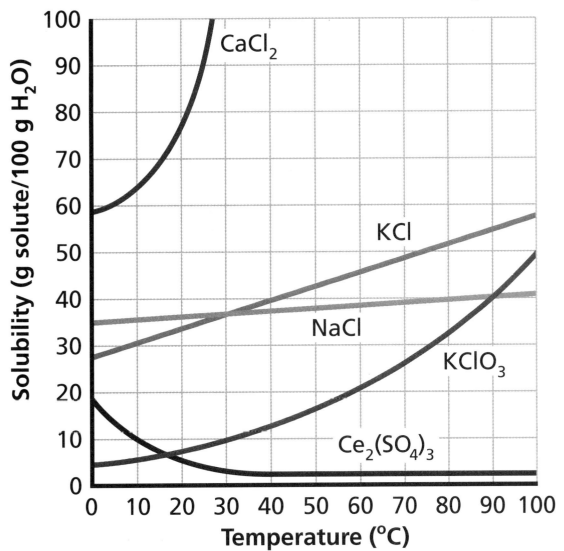

TEACHING TRANSPARENCY WORKSHEET

45

Solubility–Temperature Graphs

Use with Chapter 15, Section 15.1

1. What variables are plotted on the graph? _____

2. What is the unit of each variable?

_____

3. Use the graph to complete the table below.

Substance	Solubility at 10°C
Calcium chloride ($CaCl_2$)	
Cerium(III) sulfate ($Ce_2(SO_4)_3$)	
Potassium chloride (KCl)	
Potassium chlorate ($KClO_3$)	
Sodium chloride (NaCl)	

4. At what temperature are sodium chloride and potassium chloride equally soluble

in water? _____

5. How does the solubility of cerium(III) sulfate differ from the solubility of potassium chlorate over the temperature range 0°C–100°C?

_____

_____

_____

6. How many grams of sodium chloride will dissolve in 1.0 kg of water at 20°C?

_____

7. Explain whether increasing temperature has a greater effect on the solubility of KCl or on the solubility of NaCl.

_____

_____

_____

8. Explain how you might make a solution containing 42 g KCl dissolved in 100 g H_2O at a temperature of 40°C. What term describes this type of solution?

_____

_____

_____

TEACHING TRANSPARENCY MASTER   **46**

Phase Diagram of Solvent and Solution

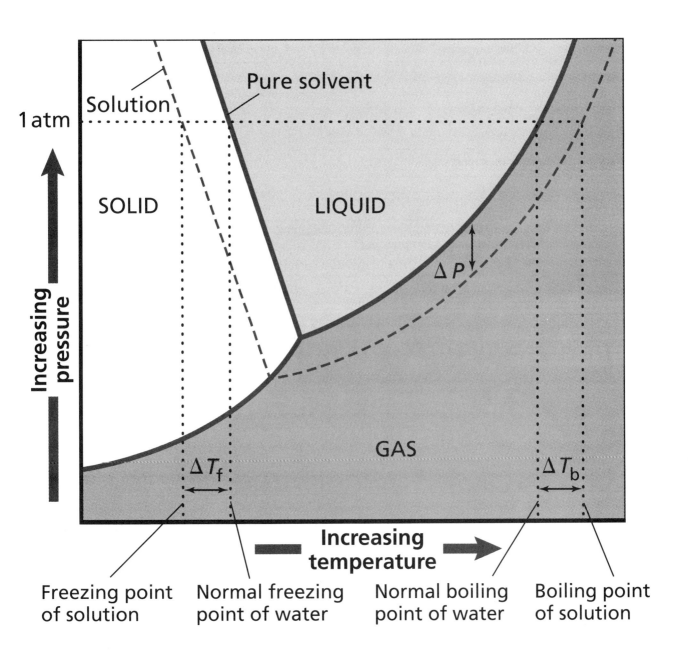

1 atm

Solution

Pure solvent

SOLID

LIQUID

ΔP

Increasing pressure

GAS

ΔT_f

ΔT_b

Increasing temperature

Freezing point of solution

Normal freezing point of water

Normal boiling point of water

Boiling point of solution

TEACHING TRANSPARENCY WORKSHEET

Phase Diagram of Solvent and Solution

Use with Chapter 15, Section 15.3

1. What variables are plotted on the phase diagram? _____

2. What solvent is represented in the phase diagram? _____

3. What phases of the solvent are represented in the diagram? _____

4. What do the solid lines represent?

   _____

   _____

5. What is the term applied to a solution in which water is the solvent? _____

6. What do the dashed lines represent?

   _____

   _____

7. At each temperature, what does ΔP represent?

   _____

   _____

8. At any temperature, how does the vapor pressure of the aqueous solution compare with the vapor pressure of the pure solvent?

   _____

   _____

9. Will a solution boil at the same temperature as the pure solvent under normal atmospheric pressure? Explain.

   _____

   _____

   _____

   _____

10. What must you do to the temperature of a solution to make it boil if it is at the boiling point of the pure solvent under normal atmospheric pressure?

    _____

11. How does the freezing point of a solution compare with the freezing point of the pure solvent at the same pressure?

    _____

Using a Calorimeter

**Use with Chapter 16,
Section 16.2**

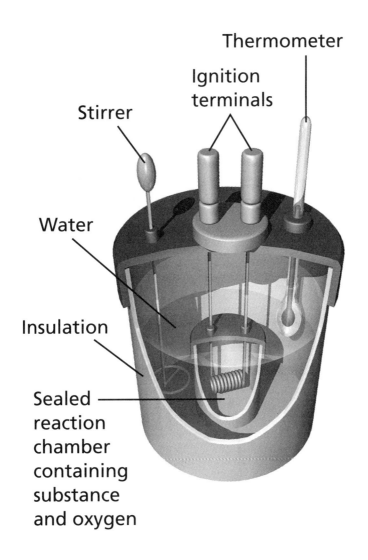

Thermometer

Ignition
terminals

Stirrer

Water

Insulation

Sealed
reaction
chamber
containing
substance
and oxygen

Name _____ Date _____ Class _____

Using a Calorimeter

**Use with Chapter 16,
Section 16.2**

1. The calorimeter shown on the transparency is used to measure the caloric content of foods. To do this, a sample of food is burned inside the reaction chamber of the calorimeter. What is the system? What are the surroundings?

_____

_____

2. What besides food must be added to the chamber? Explain why.

_____

3. What are the products of the reaction that takes place in the reaction chamber?

_____

4. Why is the calorimeter insulated?

_____

5. What does the thermometer measure?

_____

_____

6. Describe the movement of heat as the reaction takes place inside the chamber.

_____

_____

7. Assuming that no heat escapes from the calorimeter, what equation would you use to determine the amount of heat released by the burning food in the reaction chamber? Define all variables in the equation.

_____

_____

_____

8. Does the answer obtained from the equation in question 7 have a positive or negative value? Explain why. What is the sign of ΔH for the reaction?

_____

_____

TEACHING TRANSPARENCY MASTER 48

Temperature Changes of Water

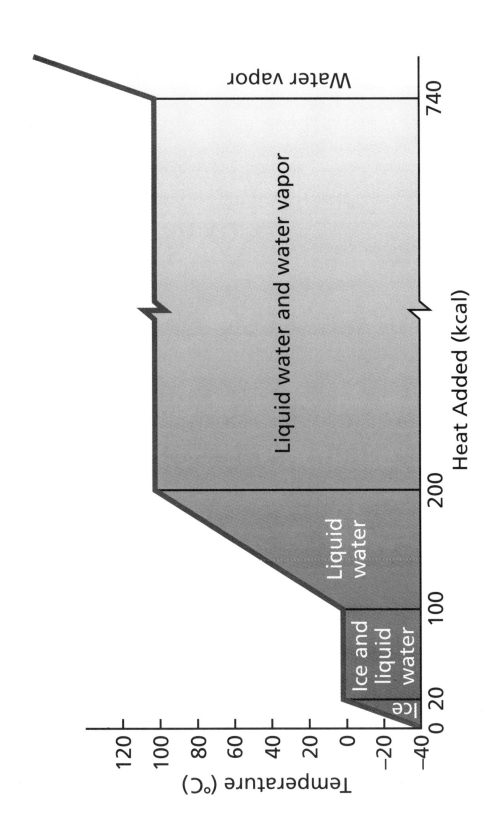

Name ______________________ Date ____________ Class ____________

TEACHING TRANSPARENCY WORKSHEET **48**

Temperature Changes of Water

Use with Chapter 16, Section 16.3

1. The graph shows what happens when ice, at −40°C, is gradually heated to more than 120°C. What is happening in the region between −40°C and 0°C?

____

____

2. At 0°C, the temperature does not change even though 80 kcal of heat is added. Why does the temperature not change?

____

____

____

3. What is happening in the region between 0°C and 100°C?

____

____

4. When the water reaches 100°C, the temperature does not change even though 540 kcal of heat is added. Why does the temperature not change?

____

____

____

5. Compare the amount of heat needed to convert liquid water to water vapor with the amount needed to convert ice to liquid water. Explain the difference.

____

____

____

____

6. What is happening in the region above 100°C?

____

____

7. If you continue to add heat, what will happen to the water vapor?

____

TEACHING TRANSPARENCY MASTER

Changes in Enthalpy and Entropy Use with Chapter 16, Sections 16.4 and 16.5

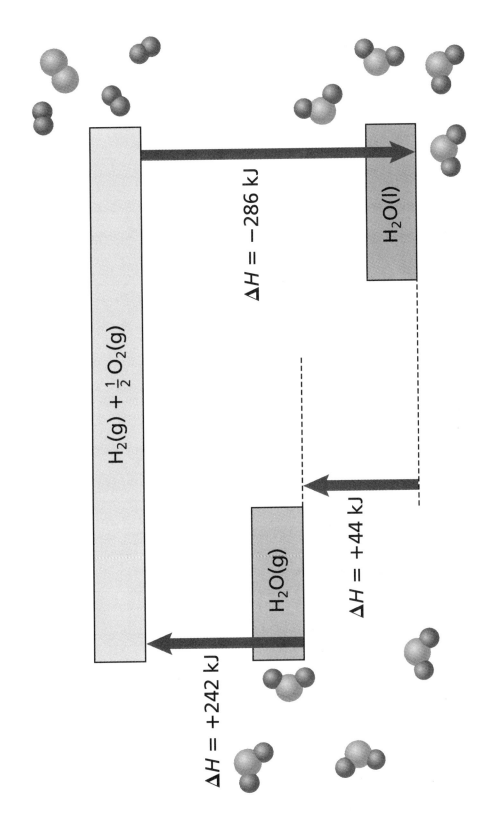

TEACHING TRANSPARENCY WORKSHEET **49**

Changes in Enthalpy and Entropy   Use with Chapter 16, Sections 16.4 and 16.5

1. What do the arrows on the transparency represent?

_____

_____

_____

2. Why do the arrows vary in direction?

_____

_____

_____

3. What can you conclude about the transitions and the magnitudes of the enthalpies shown on the transparency?

_____

_____

_____

_____

4. How does Hess's law apply to your answer to question 3?

_____

_____

_____

_____

5. What do the ball models for liquid water and gaseous water on the transparency show?

_____

_____

6. What do the ball models indicate about the overall order of the molecules?

_____

7. When molecules become more ordered or disordered, what happens to the entropy?

_____

_____

TEACHING TRANSPARENCY MASTER

Factors That Affect Reaction Rate   Use with Chapter 17, Section 17.2

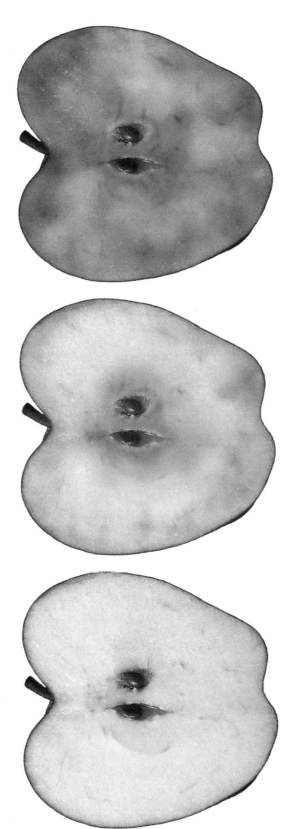

Factors That Affect Reaction Rate Use with Chapter 17, Section 17.2

1. Look at the sequence of pictures. What happened to the apple over time?

_____

2. No chemical was added to the apple. Explain why the apple changed.

_____

3. How could you test your answer to question 3?

_____

_____

_____

4. What effect would increasing the amount of air surrounding the apple have on the apple? Explain your answer.

_____

_____

_____

5. How would slicing the apple into more pieces affect the apple? Explain your answer.

_____

_____

_____

6. The apple in the pictures is raw. A cooked apple would not change the same way. Give a possible reason why.

_____

_____

_____

Reaction Order

**Use with Chapter 17,
Section 17.3**

Reaction Order

Use with Chapter 17, Section 17.3

1. What is formed when the two solutions mix?

_____

2. Explain how the substance is formed in terms of the particles in the two solutions.

_____

_____

3. On the basis of the image in the transparency, what can you conclude about the rate of the reaction? Explain your answer.

_____

_____

4. On the basis of your answer to question 3, what can you conclude about the activation energy for the reaction?

_____

5. What can you conclude about the reaction order for the reaction?

_____

_____

_____

6. If the rate equation is determined to be $k[Pb^{2+}][I^-]$, what is the reaction order?

_____

_____

7. Would you classify the reaction as exothermic, endothermic, nonspontaneous, or spontaneous. Explain your answer.

_____

_____

_____

Name _____ Date _____ Class _____

TEACHING TRANSPARENCY MASTER

52

Reaction Rate

**Use with Chapter 17,
Section 17.4**

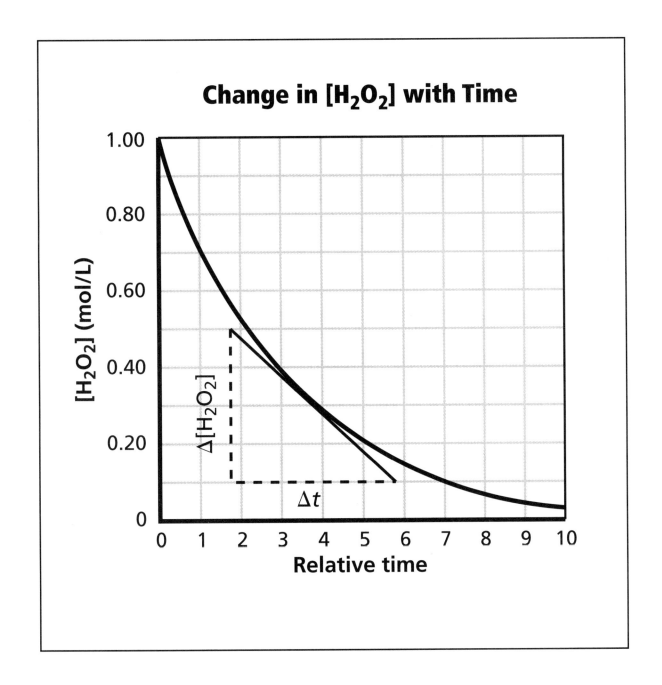

Name ______________________ Date ____________ Class ____________

TEACHING TRANSPARENCY WORKSHEET **52**

Reaction Rate

Use with Chapter 17, Section 17.4

1. What does the graph show?

____

2. Is the hydrogen peroxide a reactant or product in the reaction? How do you know?

____

____

3. The hydrogen peroxide is part of a decomposition reaction. Write a balanced equation for the reaction.

____

4. From the graph, what can you conclude about the rate of this reaction?

____

5. Define the term *instantaneous rate*.

____

6. How can you use the graph to find the instantaneous rate of the reaction that you identified in your answer to question 3? Give your answer in mathematical terms.

____

____

____

7. To show the complete relationship of reactants to products in this reaction, what else would you need to plot on the graph?

____

____

8. What would you expect your answer to question 7 to show?

____

TEACHING TRANSPARENCY MASTER **53**

Chemical Equilibrium

Ⓐ $4NH_3(g) + 5O_2(g) \rightleftharpoons 4NO(g) + 6H_2O(g)$

Ⓑ $2NO_2(g) \rightleftharpoons N_2O_4(g)$

Ⓒ $N_2(g) + 3H_2(g) \rightleftharpoons 2NH_3(g)$

Ⓓ $Ag^+(aq) + 2NH_3(aq) \rightleftharpoons Ag(NH_3)_2{}^+(aq)$

Ⓔ $2NO(g) + 2H_2(g) \rightleftharpoons N_2(g) + 2H_2O(g)$

Ⓕ $COCl_2(g) \rightleftharpoons CO(g) + Cl_2(g)$

Ⓖ $HCN(aq) + H_2O(l) \rightleftharpoons H_3O^+(aq) + CN^-(aq)$

Ⓗ $H_2O(g) + CO(g) \rightleftharpoons H_2(g) + CO_2(g)$

Chemical Equilibrium

**Use with Chapter 18,
Section 18.1**

1. Write the equilibrium constant expressions for the reactions on the transparency.

A _____   E _____

B _____   F _____

C _____   G _____

D _____   H _____

2. What is heterogeneous equilibrium?

_____

_____

3. Which equilibrium reactions are homogeneous equilibriums?

_____

_____

4. Which equilibrium reaction is a heterogeneous equilibrium?

_____

_____

5. When writing equilibrium constant expressions, pure solids and liquids are not included. Why? Why do you include all reactants of equation D in its equilibrium constant expression?

_____

_____

_____

_____

6. If the K_{eq} for one of the reactions was 35.6, what would you know about the equilibrium?

_____

_____

TEACHING TRANSPARENCY MASTER

54

How Changing Concentration Affects Equilibrium

$$CO(g) + 3H_2(g) \rightleftharpoons CH_4(g) + H_2O(g)$$

❶ $CO(g) + 3H_2(g) \longrightarrow\!\rightleftharpoons CH_4(g) + H_2O(g)$

$CO(g)$

❷ $CO(g) + 3H_2(g) \longrightarrow\!\rightleftharpoons CH_4(g) + H_2O(g)$

$H_2O(g)$

❸ $CO(g) + 3H_2(g) \rightleftharpoons\!\longleftarrow CH_4(g) + H_2O(g)$

❹ $CO(g) + 3H_2(g) \rightleftharpoons\!\longleftarrow CH_4(g) + H_2O(g)$

$H_2O(g)$

Name _____ Date _____ Class _____

How Changing Concentration Affects Equilibrium

Use with Chapter 18, Section 18.2

1. Why do the changes shown in equations 1 and 2 cause the equilibrium to move to the right? What other changes in concentration would also cause a shift to the right?

_____

_____

_____

_____

_____

2. Why do the changes shown in equations 3 and 4 cause the equilibrium to move to the left? What other changes in concentration would also cause a shift to the left?

_____

_____

_____

_____

_____

3. What effect would decreasing the volume of the reaction container have on the equilibrium? Why?

_____

_____

_____

_____

4. When does changing the volume of the reaction container not affect the equilibrium?

_____

_____

5. The production of methane and water vapor from carbon monoxide and hydrogen gas is an exothermic reaction. What does this tell you about how an increase in temperature would affect the equilibrium of this reaction? How would it affect the equilibrium constant?

_____

_____

_____

6. When does changing the temperature not affect a reaction at equilibrium?

_____

TEACHING TRANSPARENCY MASTER 55

Ionization of a Triprotic Acid

Use with Chapter 19,
Section 19.1

$$H_3AsO_4(aq) + H_2O(l) \rightleftharpoons H_3O^+(aq) + H_2AsO_4^-(aq)$$

$$H_2AsO_4^-(aq) + H_2O(l) \rightleftharpoons H_3O^+(aq) + HAsO_4^{2-}(aq)$$

$$HAsO_4^{2-}(aq) + H_2O(l) \rightleftharpoons H_3O^+(aq) + AsO_4^{3-}(aq)$$

Name ____________________ Date ____________ Class ____________

TEACHING TRANSPARENCY WORKSHEET **55**

Ionization of a Triprotic Acid

Use with Chapter 19, Section 19.1

1. H_3AsO_4 is a triprotic acid. What does the term *triprotic* mean?

____

2. What do all three of these equations have in common?

____

____

3. What property of water causes the ionization of H_3AsO_4 in aqueous solution?

____

____

4. Which step would require the least energy? Explain.

____

____

____

5. Why are double arrows used in the questions shown?

____

____

____

6. Write a similar set of equations for the complete ionization of phosphoric acid (H_3PO_4), which is another triprotic acid.

____

____

7. The formula for citric acid is $H_3C_6H_5O_7$. How many steps would occur in the complete ionization of citric acid? Explain.

____

____

____

Ionization Equations and Constants

Use with Chapter 19, Section 19.2

Ionization Constants for Weak Acids

Acid	Ionization equation	K_a (298 K)
Hydrosulfuric	$H_2S \rightleftharpoons H^+ + HS^-$	8.9×10^{-8}
	$HS^- \rightleftharpoons H^+ + S^{2-}$	1×10^{-19}
Phosphoric	$H_3PO_4 \rightleftharpoons H^+ + H_2PO_4^-$	7.5×10^{-3}
	$H_2PO_4^- \rightleftharpoons H^+ + HPO_4^{2-}$	6.2×10^{-8}
	$HPO_4^{2-} \rightleftharpoons H^+ + PO_4^{3-}$	2.2×10^{-13}
Hydrofluoric	$HF \rightleftharpoons H^+ + F^-$	6.3×10^{-4}
Methanoic	$HCOOH \rightleftharpoons H^+ + HCOO^-$	1.8×10^{-4}
Ethanoic (Acetic)	$CH_3COOH \rightleftharpoons H^+ + CH_3COO^-$	1.8×10^{-5}
Carbonic	$H_2CO_3 \rightleftharpoons H^+ + HCO_3^-$	4.5×10^{-7}
	$HCO_3^- \rightleftharpoons H^+ + CO_3^{2-}$	4.7×10^{-11}
Hypochlorous	$HClO \rightleftharpoons H^+ + ClO^-$	4.0×10^{-8}

TEACHING TRANSPARENCY WORKSHEET **56**

Ionization Equations and Constants

Use with Chapter 19, Section 19.2

1. Why do some acids have more than one ionization equation?

_____

_____

2. How do you know that the acids listed in the table are listed from strongest to weakest?

_____

_____

3. Which is stronger, the conjugate base of carbonic acid or the conjugate base of phosphoric acid? Explain.

_____

_____

_____

4. Write all the ionization equations for phosphorous acid (H_3PO_3), a weak acid.

_____

_____

_____

5. Write the ionization constant expression for these acids.

  a. hypochlorous acid _____

  b. methanoic acid _____

6. Why can you assume that the concentrations of the ions in the ionization constant expression for a weak acid are equal?

_____

_____

TEACHING TRANSPARENCY MASTER

57

The pH Scale

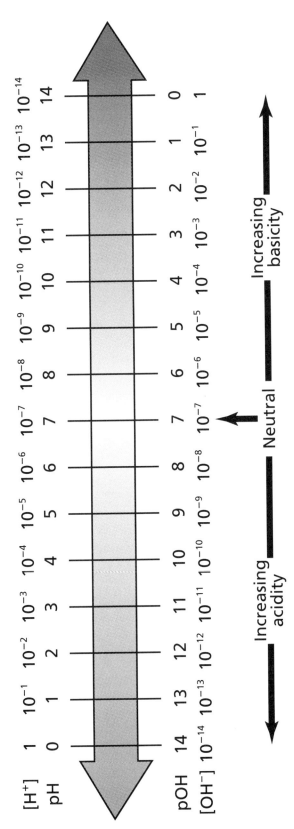

TEACHING TRANSPARENCY WORKSHEET 57

The pH Scale

1. What is the pH of a solution with a $[H^+]$ of 10^{-8}? _____

2. What is the pOH of a solution with a $[OH^-]$ of 10^{-11}? _____

3. What is the pH of a solution that has a $[OH^-]$ of 10^{-2}? _____

4. What is the pOH of a solution that has a $[H^+]$ of 10^{-5}? _____

5. What do you notice about the product of $[H^+]$ and $[OH^-]$ for any aqueous solution?

    _____

6. What do you notice about the sum of pH and pOH for any aqueous solution?

    _____

7. Which is more acidic, a solution with a pH of 6 or one with a pH of 9?

    _____

8. Which is more basic, a solution with a pOH of 7 or one with a pOH of 12?

    _____

9. Which is more acidic, a solution with a pH of 5 or one with a pOH of 10?

    _____

10. Which is more basic, a solution with a pH of 8 or one with a pOH of 12?

    _____

11. Stomach contents can have a pH of 3. Are stomach contents acidic, basic, or neutral?

    _____

12. Pure water has a pOH of 7. Is pure water acidic, basic, or neutral?

    _____

13. Normal rain has a pH of approximately 6. Is normal rain strongly acidic, slightly acidic, neutral, slightly basic, or strongly basic?

    _____

14. Acid precipitation is often a problem in industrialized areas. What might you expect the pH of acid rain to be?

    _____

Titration Graphs

Use with Chapter 19,
Section 19.4

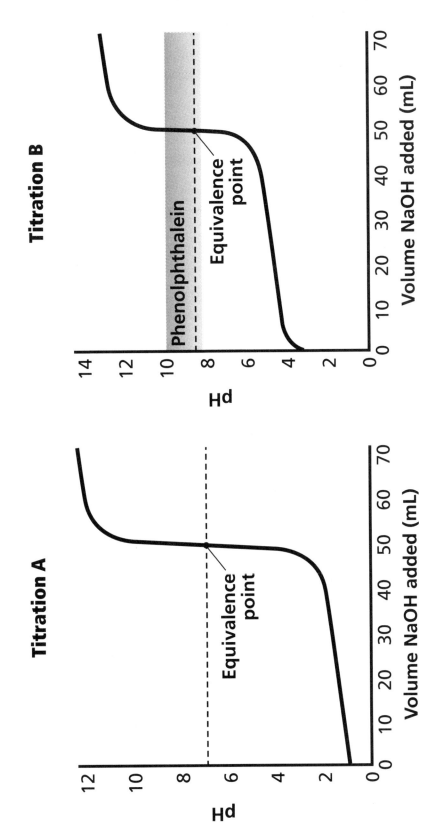

TEACHING TRANSPARENCY WORKSHEET   **58**

Titration Graphs

Use with Chapter 19, Section 19.4

1. NaOH is a strong base, HCl is a strong acid, and HCOOH is a weak acid.

   a. Which titration is between a strong acid and a strong base?

   _____

   b. Which titration is between a weak acid and a strong base?

   _____

2. What generalization can be made about the pH of the solution resulting from a complete reaction between a strong acid and a strong base?

_____

3. Does the graph for Titration A support your answer to question 2? Explain.

_____

_____

4. What generalization can be made about the pH of the solution resulting from a complete reaction between a strong base and a weak acid?

_____

5. Does the graph for Titration B support your answer to question 4? Explain.

_____

_____

6. During Titration A, what was the pH after 40.0 mL of NaOH was added to the HCl?

_____

7. What was the pH after 40.0 mL of NaOH was added to the HCOOH during Titration B?

_____

8. From the curves of the titrations, explain how you would know the equivalence point was near if a pH meter was used instead of an indicator.

_____

9. Why was phenolphthalein a better choice for an indicator in Titration B than it would have been for Titration A?

_____

_____

_____

Oxidation and Reduction

**Use with Chapter 20,
Section 20.1**

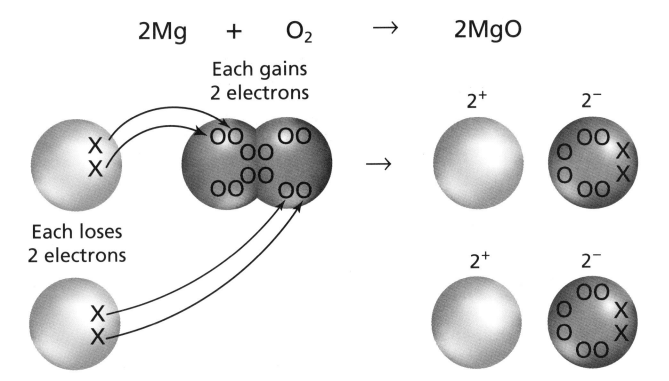

$$2Mg \quad + \quad O_2 \quad \rightarrow \quad 2MgO$$

Each gains
2 electrons

Each loses
2 electrons

Oxidation and Reduction

Use with Chapter 20, Section 20.1

1. How do you know that the reaction for the chemical equation shown on the transparency is a redox reaction?

_____

2. What element is oxidized? _____

3. How do you know the element is oxidized?

_____

4. What ion is formed as the result of this oxidation? _____

5. What element is reduced? _____

6. How do you know the element is reduced?

_____

7. What ion is formed as the result of this reduction? _____

8. How many electrons were transferred during this reaction as it is shown? Explain.

_____

9. Assuming the atoms shown are the only ones available, could magnesium atoms be oxidized if oxygen atoms were not reduced? Explain.

_____

10. Draw a diagram similar to the one on the transparency to show what happens during the redox reaction between one atom of magnesium and a fluorine molecule.

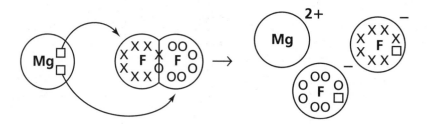

11. In the reaction from question 10, what element is oxidized? _____

12. What ion is formed from this oxidation? _____

13. What element is reduced? _____

14. What ion is formed from this reduction? _____

15. How many electrons were transferred during this reaction as it is shown? Explain.

_____

TEACHING TRANSPARENCY MASTER

60

Equations for Redox Reactions

**Use with Chapter 20,
Section 20.1**

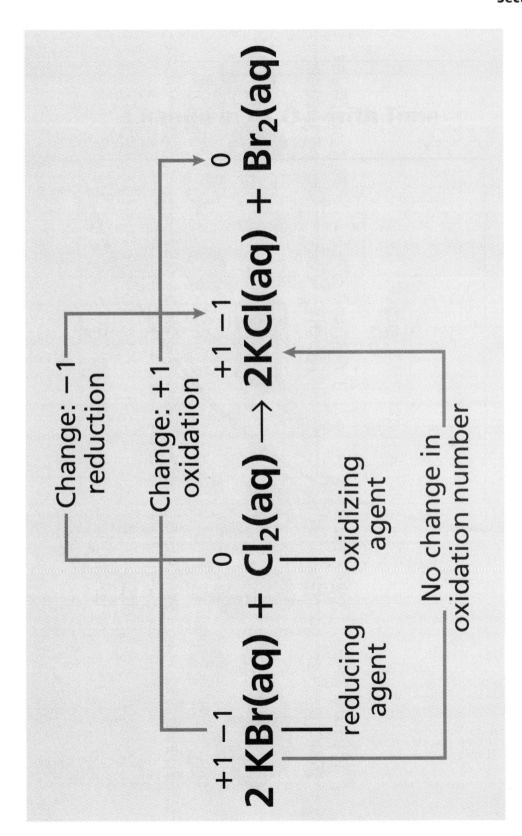

TEACHING TRANSPARENCY WORKSHEET   **60**

Equations for Redox Reactions

Use with Chapter 20, Section 20.1

1. Did the bromide ion accept or donate an electron in this reaction? How do you know?

_____

_____

2. Locate the ion that has no change in oxidation number in this reaction.

   a. What is the term applied to an ion that is present but does not enter into the actual

   chemical reaction? _____

   b. What ion in this equation is this type of ion? _____

3. Write the balanced net ionic equation for this reaction. What ion in the complete chemi-cal equation is not included in the net ionic equation?

_____

_____

4. What generalization can you make about what happens to an oxidizing agent during a redox reaction? Explain.

_____

_____

5. What generalization can you make about what happens to a reducing agent during a redox reaction? Explain.

_____

_____

6. Compare what happens in the equation on the transparency to what happens in the following equation:

$$Fe(s) + 2HCl(aq) \rightarrow FeCl_2(aq) + H_2(g)$$

   a. Assign an oxidation number to each ion, atom, or molecule shown in the above equation.

   _____

   b. What is oxidized? _____

   c. What is reduced? _____

   d. What is the oxidizing agent? _____

   e. What is the reducing agent? _____

   f. What has no change in oxidation number? _____

Teaching Transparency Worksheets

Balancing Equations: Oxidation-Number Method

Use with Chapter 20, Section 20.2

How to Balance Equations for Redox Reactions by the Oxidation-Number Method

❶ Write a chemical equation for the reaction, showing all reactants and products.

❷ Determine the oxidation number of each element shown in the equation. Remember to treat a polyatomic ion as a single ion if it remains unchanged.

❸ Draw a line connecting the atoms involved in oxidation and another line connecting the atoms involved in reduction. Write the net change in oxidation number above or below each line.

❹ Calculate coefficients to balance the number of electrons transferred in the redox part of the reaction.

❺ If necessary, use the conventional method of balancing equations to balance all atoms and charges.

Name ______________________ Date ____________ Class ____________

TEACHING TRANSPARENCY WORKSHEET **61**

Balancing Equations: Oxidation-Number Method

Use with Chapter 20, Section 20.2

1. Use the rules shown on the transparency to balance the equation for the reaction that occurs when you place solid magnesium into nitric acid (HNO_3). Aqueous magnesium nitrate and hydrogen gas form.

a. Step 1: ______________________

b. Step 2:

c. Step 3:

d. Step 4: ______________________

e. Step 5: ______________________

2. Use the rules shown on the transparency to balance the equation for the reaction that occurs when you mix solutions of nitric acid (HNO_3), potassium chromate (K_2CrO_4), and iron(II) nitrate ($Fe(NO_3))_3$. Aqueous potassium nitrate, iron(III) nitrate, and chromium(III) nitrate form, along with water.

a. Step 1: ______________________

b. Step 2:

c. Step 3:

d. Step 4: ______________________

e. Step 5: ______________________

TEACHING TRANSPARENCY MASTER 62

Half-Reactions

Use with Chapter 20,
Section 20.3

Various Oxidation–Reduction Reactions in Which Iron Is Oxidized

Overall reaction	Oxidation half-reaction	Reduction half-reaction
A. $Fe + O_2 \rightarrow Fe_2O_3$	$Fe \rightarrow Fe^{3+} + 3e^-$	$O_2 + 4e^- \rightarrow 2O^{2-}$
B. $Fe + Cl_2 \rightarrow FeCl_3$	$Fe \rightarrow Fe^{3+} + 3e^-$	$Cl_2 + 2e^- \rightarrow 2Cl^-$
C. $Fe + F_2 \rightarrow FeF_3$	$Fe \rightarrow Fe^{3+} + 3e^-$	$F_2 + 2e^- \rightarrow 2F^-$
D. $Fe + HBr \rightarrow FeBr_3 + H_2$	$Fe \rightarrow Fe^{3+} + 3e^-$	$2H^+ + 2e^- \rightarrow H_2$
E. $Fe + AgNO_3 \rightarrow Fe(NO_3)_3 + Ag$	$Fe \rightarrow Fe^{3+} + 3e^-$	$Ag^+ + e^- \rightarrow Ag$
F. $Fe + CuSO_4 \rightarrow Cu + Fe_2(SO_4)_3$	$Fe \rightarrow Fe^{3+} + 3e^-$	$Cu^{2+} + 2e^- \rightarrow Cu$

Balancing Equation A in the Table by the Half-Reaction Method:

Step 1	Rewrite the equation in complete ionic form. Do not include any coefficients. $$Fe + O_2 \rightarrow Fe^{3+} + O^{2-}$$
Step 2	Remove any spectator ions from the equation to derive the net ionic equation. **None are present in this equation.**
Step 3	Write half-reactions for the redox reaction, showing the correct number of atoms indicated by the net ionic equation and the number of electrons lost or accepted. **Oxidation: $Fe \rightarrow Fe^{3+} + 3e^-$; Reduction: $O_2 + 4e^- \rightarrow 2O^{2-}$**
Step 4	Balance the atoms of each type and the number of electrons lost and the number of electrons gained in the half-reactions. **Oxidation: $4(Fe \rightarrow Fe^{3+} + 3e^-) = 4Fe \rightarrow 4Fe^{3+} + 12e^-$** **Reduction: $3(O_2 + 4e^- \rightarrow 2O^{2-}) = 3O_2 + 12e^- \rightarrow 6O^{2-}$**
Step 5	Combine half-reactions into one complete equation. $$4Fe + 3O_2 + 12e^- \rightarrow 4Fe^{3+} + 6O^{2-} + 12e^-$$
Step 6	Simplify the equation by combining like terms. $$4Fe + 3O_2 + 12e^- \rightarrow 4Fe^{3+} + 6O^{2-} + 12e^-$$
Step 7	Complete the equation by returning any spectator ions, writing formulas as they were in the original equation, and balancing any non-redox parts of the equation. $$4Fe + 3O_2 \rightarrow 2Fe_2O_3$$
Step 8	Check all atoms on both sides of the equation to be sure the equation is balanced. **The equation is balanced.**

TEACHING TRANSPARENCY WORKSHEET **62**

Half-Reactions

**Use with Chapter 20,
Section 20.3**

1. In terms of electron transfer, what has happened in all of the oxidation half-reactions listed in the table?

    _____

2. In terms of electron transfer, what has happened in all of the reduction half-reactions listed in the table?

    _____

3. In all of these reactions, iron metal is oxidized. Is iron metal ever reduced? Explain.

    _____

    _____

4. Can iron ions be oxidized? Can they be reduced? Explain.

    _____

    _____

    _____

5. In which of the reactions shown in the table are spectator ions present? For each reaction that contains a spectator ion, identify the spectator ion.

    _____

6. Use the half-reaction method to balance equations B–F from the table.

    B. $Fe + Cl_2 \rightarrow FeCl_3$

    C. $Fe + F_2 \rightarrow FeF_3$

    D. $Fe + HBr \rightarrow FeBr_3 + H_2$

    E. $Fe + AgNO_3 \rightarrow Fe(NO_3)_3 + Ag$

    F. $Fe + CuSO_4 \rightarrow Cu + Fe_2(SO_4)_3$

Electrochemical Cell

**Use with Chapter 21,
Section 21.1**

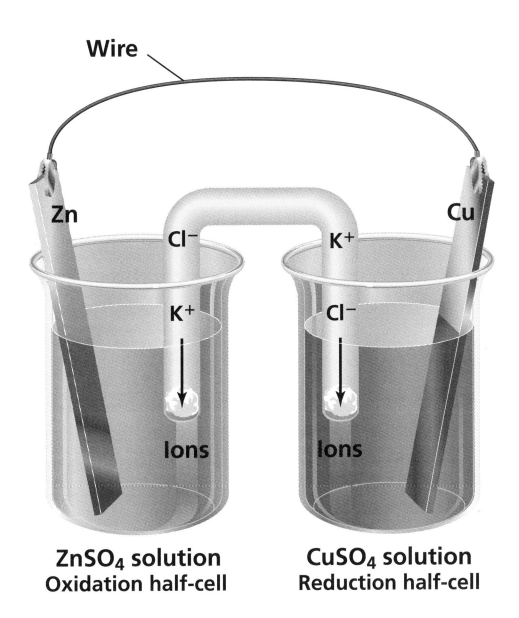

Wire

Zn

Cu

Cl⁻

K⁺

K⁺

Cl⁻

Ions

Ions

ZnSO₄ solution
Oxidation half-cell

CuSO₄ solution
Reduction half-cell

TEACHING TRANSPARENCY WORKSHEET   63

Electrochemical Cell

1. What half-cell reaction takes place in each beaker?

Left beaker _____

Right beaker _____

2. What type of reaction (oxidation or reduction) takes place in each beaker?

Left beaker _____   Right beaker _____

3. Which electrode is the anode and which is the cathode?

Anode _____   Cathode _____

4. What atomic particles move through the wire, and in which direction do they move?

_____

5. Which ions flow from the salt bridge into each beaker?

Left beaker _____   Right beaker _____

6. Write the overall cell reaction.

_____

7. Represent the cell symbolically, using vertical lines to separate the components.

_____

8. Use the following standard reduction potentials to calculate the standard cell potential, E^0_{cell}.

$$Zn^{2+} + 2e^- \rightarrow Zn \qquad\qquad Cu^{2+} + 2e^- \rightarrow Cu$$

$$E^0_{Zn} = -0.7618 \text{ V} \qquad\qquad E^0_{Cu} = +0.3419 \text{ V}$$

_____

9. How is an electrochemical cell useful?

_____

_____

Hydrogen–Oxygen Fuel Cell

**Use with Chapter 21,
Section 21.2**

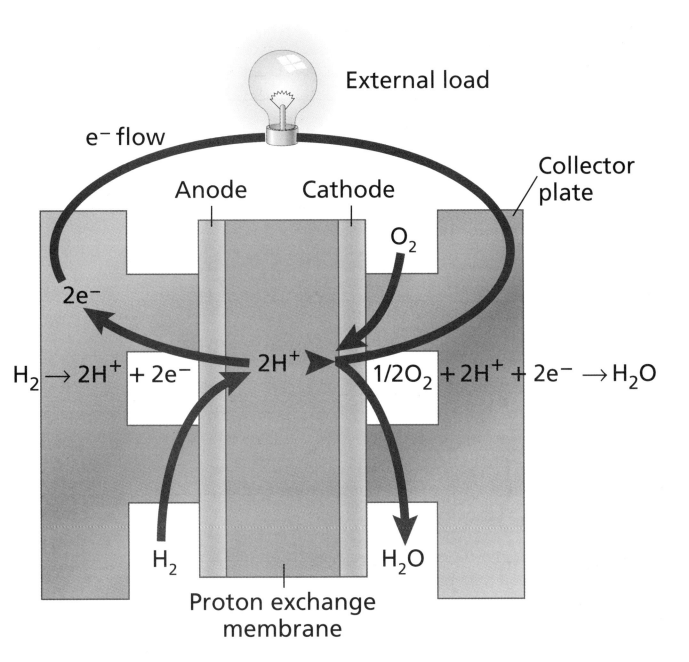

External load

e^- flow

Anode   Cathode

Collector
plate

O_2

$2e^-$

$2H^+$

$H_2 \rightarrow 2H^+ + 2e^-$ $1/2O_2 + 2H^+ + 2e^- \rightarrow H_2O$

H_2 H_2O

Proton exchange
membrane

Hydrogen–Oxygen Fuel Cell

**Use with Chapter 21,
Section 21.2**

1. What half-cell reaction takes place in the anode?

_____

2. What half-cell reaction takes place in the cathode?

_____

3. What type of reaction (oxidation or reduction) takes place in the anode and in the cathode?

anode _____   cathode _____

4. Write the overall cell reaction.

_____

5. Represent the cell symbolically, using vertical lines to separate the components.

_____

6. Use the following standard reduction potentials to calculate the standard cell potential, E^0_{cell}.

$$2H^+ + 2e^- \rightarrow H_2 \qquad\qquad \tfrac{1}{2}O_2 + 2H^+ + 2e^- \rightarrow H_2O$$
$$E^0 = 0.0000 \qquad\qquad\qquad E^0 = +1.229 \text{ V}$$

_____

7. What is the main useful product of the hydrogen–oxygen fuel cell?

_____

8. Compare and contrast this cell reaction with the burning of hydrogen in air.

_____

_____

_____

_____

Electrolysis of Brine

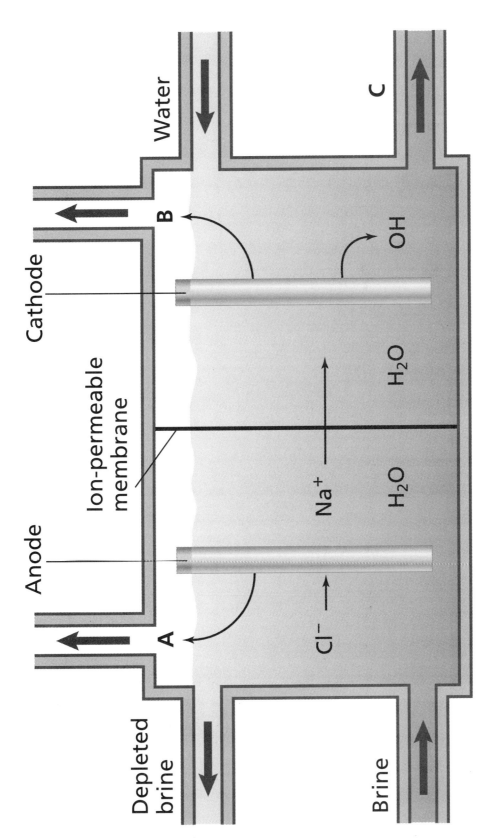

TEACHING TRANSPARENCY WORKSHEET **65**

Electrolysis of Brine

**Use with Chapter 21,
Section 21.3**

1. What two half-cell reactions are possible at the anode?

_____

_____

2. Which of these two reactions is more likely to occur at the anode if a high concentration of chloride ions is present? Why?

_____

_____

3. What two half-cell reactions are possible at the cathode?

_____

_____

4. Which of these two reactions is more likely to occur at the cathode? Why?

_____

5. Write the overall cell reaction.

_____

6. Identify the products labeled A, B, and C on the transparency. (Hint: A and B are gases.)

A _____   **B** _____   **C** _____

7. Why is the hydrolysis of brine useful?

_____

_____

8. What must be done to cause the hydrolysis of brine to occur?

_____

_____

9. In what geographic areas do you think it would be most economical to set up this process? Why?

_____

_____

TEACHING TRANSPARENCY MASTER 66

Isomers

A

$$\underset{CH_3CH_2CH_2}{\overset{H}{\diagdown}}C=C\underset{H}{\overset{CH_2CH_2CH_3}{\diagup}}$$

$$\underset{CH_3CH_2CH_2}{\overset{H}{\diagdown}}C=C\underset{CH_2CH_2CH_3}{\overset{H}{\diagup}}$$

B

$$\underset{CH_3CH_2CH_2CH_2}{\overset{H}{\diagdown}}C=C\underset{H}{\overset{H}{\diagup}}$$

$$\underset{CH_3CH_2CH_2}{\overset{H}{\diagdown}}C=C\underset{CH_3}{\overset{H}{\diagup}}$$

C

$$CH_3CH_2CH_2CHCH_3$$
$$\qquad\qquad\quad |$$
$$\qquad\qquad\quad CH_3$$

$$\qquad\qquad CH_3$$
$$\qquad\qquad |$$
$$CH_3CH_2CHCH_2CH_3$$

D

$$\qquad\qquad\quad CH_2CH_3$$
$$\qquad\qquad\qquad |$$
$$CH_3CH_2CH_2-C-CH_3$$
$$\qquad\qquad\qquad |$$
$$\qquad\qquad\qquad H$$

$$\qquad\qquad\quad CH_2CH_2CH_3$$
$$\qquad\qquad\qquad |$$
$$CH_3CH_2-C-CH_3$$
$$\qquad\qquad\quad |$$
$$\qquad\qquad\quad H$$

E

$$\qquad\quad CH_3$$
$$\qquad\quad |$$
$$CH_3CH_2CCH_3$$
$$\qquad\quad |$$
$$\qquad\quad CH_3$$

$$CH_3CH_2CH_2CH_2CH_2CH_3$$

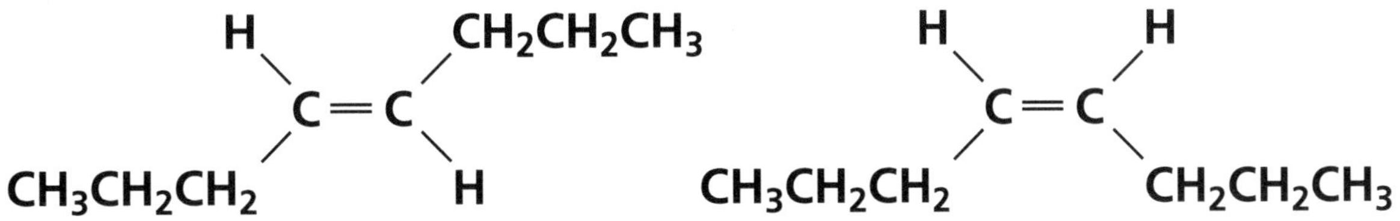

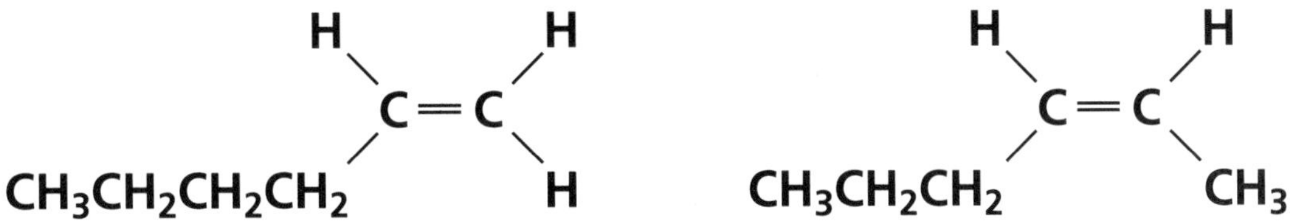

TEACHING TRANSPARENCY WORKSHEET 66

Isomers

Use with Chapter 22, Section 22.4

1. Which pair(s) of isomers represent structural isomers?

---

2. Which pair(s) of isomers represent stereoisomers?

---

3. Which pair(s) of isomers represent geometric isomers?

---

4. Which pair(s) of isomers represent optical isomers?

---

5. Which pair(s) of isomers would you expect to have different melting points, boiling points, and densities?

---

6. Which pair(s) of isomers would you expect to have different chemical properties? (Include properties related to chemical reactions where chirality is important.)

---

7. Which pair(s) of isomers would rotate the plane of polarized light in opposite directions?

---

8. Name the isomers in pair E.

---

9. Which isomer in pair A is in the *cis-* form, the one on the left or the one on the right?

---

10. Which pair(s) of isomers have an asymmetric carbon?

Name _____   Date _____   Class _____

Structure of Benzene

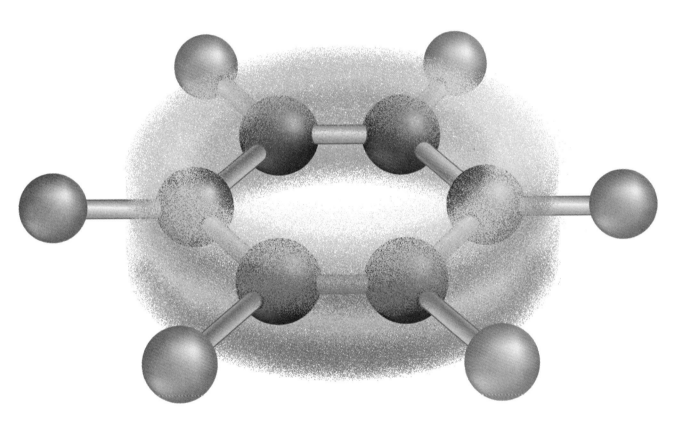

TEACHING TRANSPARENCY WORKSHEET

67

Structure of Benzene

**Use with Chapter 22,
Section 22.4**

1. How many carbon atoms and hydrogen atoms does a molecule of benzene have?

_____

2. Is benzene a saturated hydrocarbon?

_____

3. What does the double-donut shape on the transparency represent?

_____

_____

4. The drawing below shows what Kekulé proposed for the structure of benzene. How is this structure similar to the structure shown on the transparency?

_____

_____

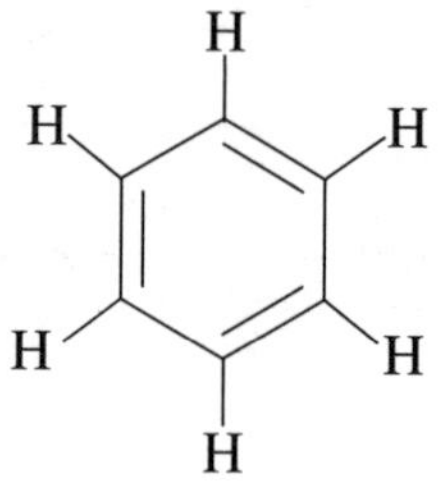

5. How does the structure proposed by Kekulé differ from the structure shown on the transparency?

_____

_____

_____

6. If the structure proposed by Kekulé actually existed, would you expect it to be more reactive or less reactive than benzene? Why?

_____

_____

_____

7. In the space below, draw another way to represent the structure of benzene that agrees with what chemists know about the properties of benzene.

Name _____ Date _____ Class _____

Naming Halocarbons

Use with Chapter 23,
Section 23.1

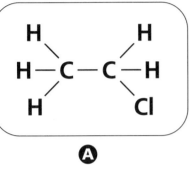

A

B

C

D

E

F

G

H

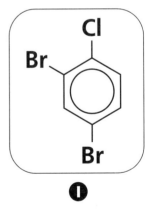

I

TEACHING TRANSPARENCY WORKSHEET   68

Naming Halocarbons

**Use with Chapter 23,
Section 23.1**

1. What is the name for any non-carbon or non-hydrogen group, such as a halogen, that is present in an organic molecule and reacts in a certain way?

   _____

2. What is the name for any halocarbon in which the halogen is covalently bonded to an aliphatic carbon atom?

   _____

3. What is the name of the compound labeled A? Would the movement of the chlorine atom to another position on the two-carbon chain create a different compound?

   _____

4. What is the name of compound B? Why are numbers necessary in naming it?

   _____

   _____

   _____

5. What is the name of compound C? Compare the name of compound C to that of compound B, and explain your answer.

   _____

   _____

6. What is the name of compound D? _____

7. What rule is followed in naming halocarbons that have two different types of halogens? How are the numbers assigned?

   _____

   _____

8. What is the name of compound E? _____

9. What is the name of compound F? _____

10. What is the name of compound G? _____

11. What is the name for any halocarbon in which the halogen is covalently bonded to a benzene ring or other aromatic group?

   _____

12. What is the name of compound H? _____

13. What is the name of compound I?

   _____

TEACHING TRANSPARENCY MASTER

Alcohols, Ethers, and Amines

Use with Chapter 23, Section 23.2

A

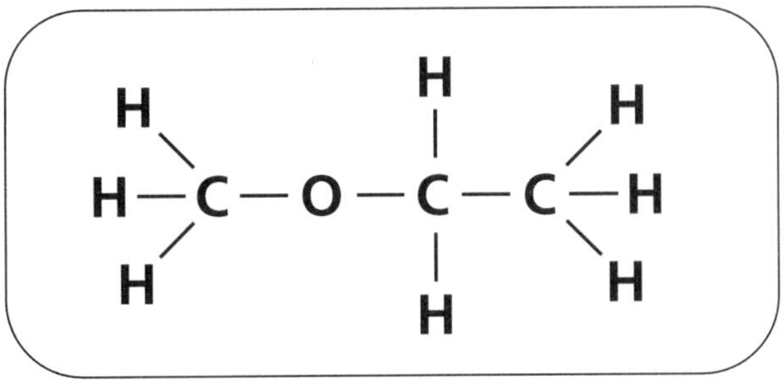

B

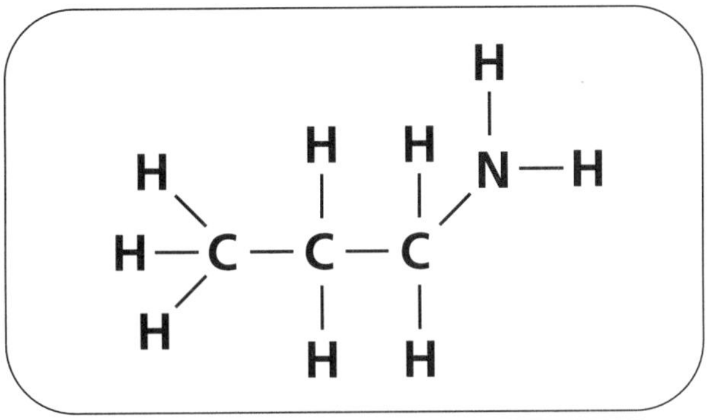

C

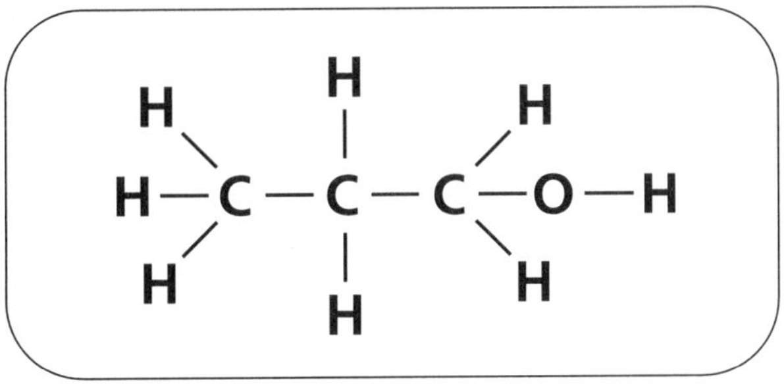

D

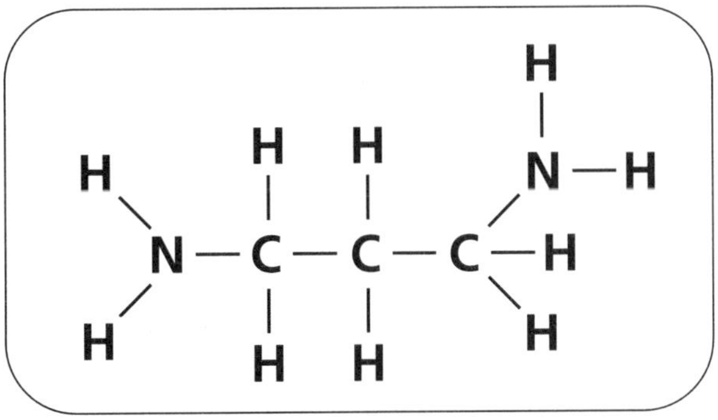

E

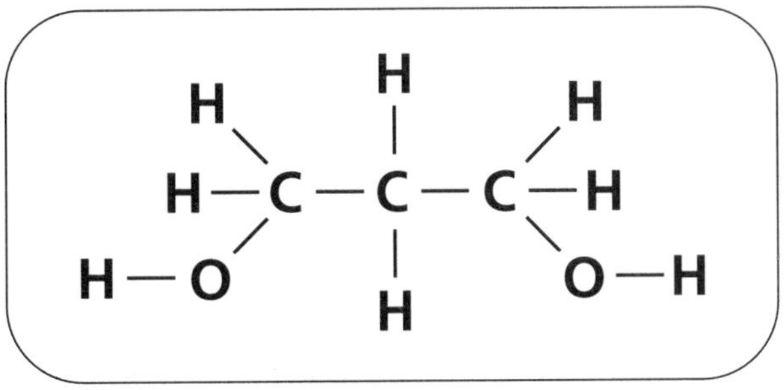

TEACHING TRANSPARENCY WORKSHEET

Alcohols, Ethers, and Amines

Use with Chapter 23, Section 23.2

1. What are the name and formula of the functional group in alcohols?

_____

2. With what suffix do the names of alcohols end?

_____

3. How is the position of the functional group indicated in naming alcohols?

_____

4. What structure is characteristic of ether molecules?

_____

5. In naming ethers, what rule is applied if an ether's alkyl groups are different?

_____

6. What structure is characteristic of amine molecules?

_____

7. Name the compounds labeled A–E.

compound A _____

compound B _____

compound C _____

compound D _____

compound E _____

8. Of compounds A, B, and C, which is likely to be a weak base?

_____

9. Of compounds A, B, and C, which is likely to have the lowest boiling point?

_____

10. Of compounds A, B, and C, which is most likely to have an offensive odor?

_____

Name ______________________ Date ____________ Class ____________

TEACHING TRANSPARENCY MASTER 70

Carbonyl, Carboxyl, and Amide Groups

Use with Chapter 23, Section 23.3

A

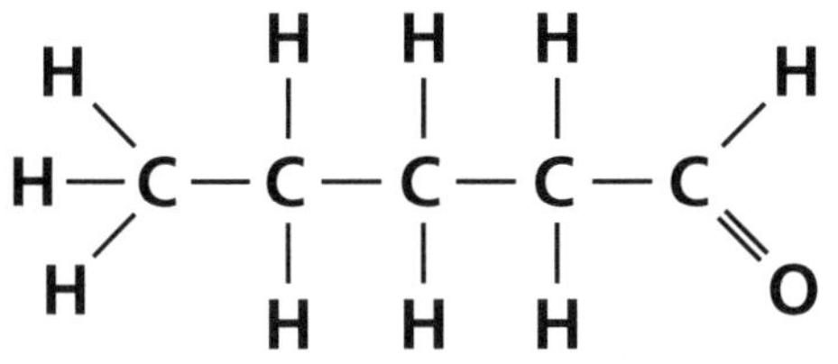

B

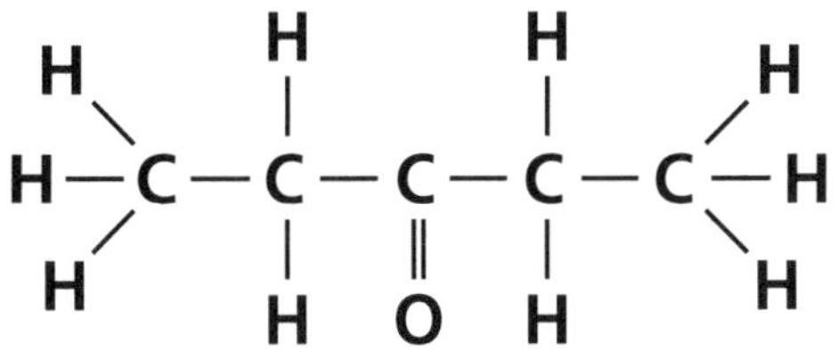

C

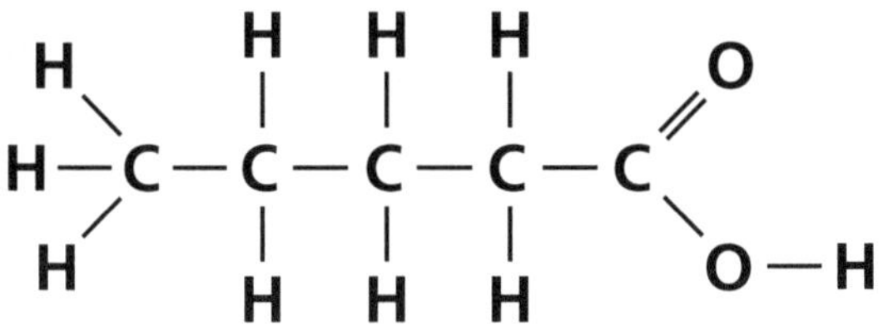

D

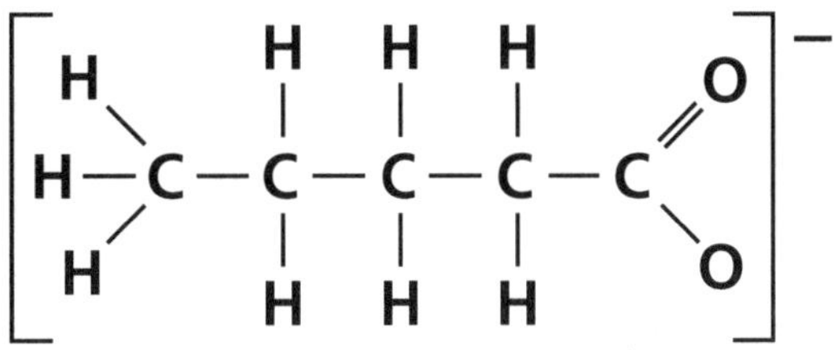

E

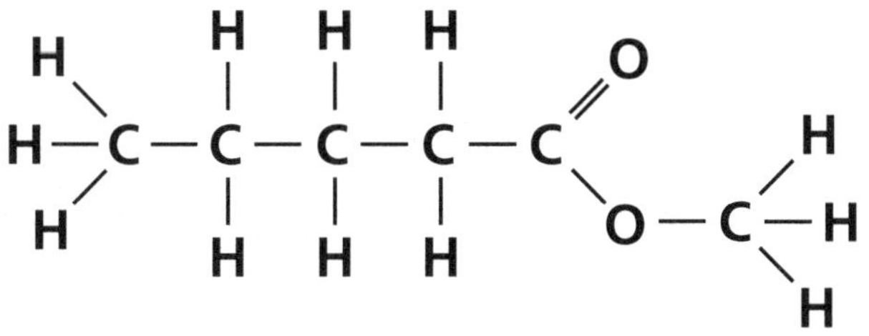

F

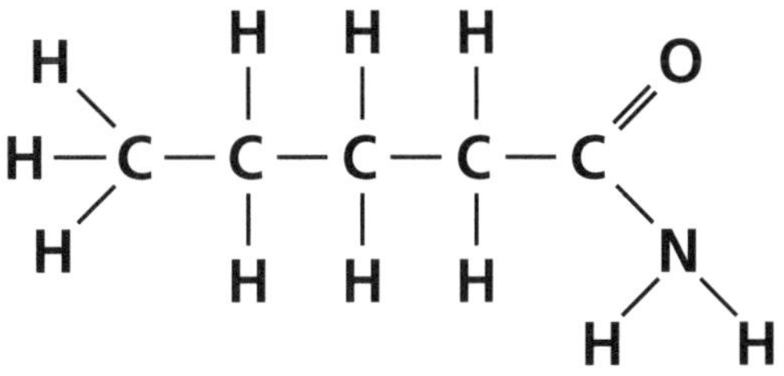

TEACHING TRANSPARENCY WORKSHEET (70)

Carbonyl, Carboxyl, and Amide Groups

Use with Chapter 23, Section 23.3

1. What is the name of the functional structural group that all the compounds shown have in common? Describe that structure.

_____

_____

2. The following questions apply to the compound labeled A on the transparency.

   a. What is the name of the compound? _____

   b. To what category of organic compound (carboxylic acid, ketone, ester, amide, or

      aldehyde) does it belong? _____

   c. State whether you would expect this compound to be polar and whether it can form hydrogen bonds with water. Also, predict whether the compound's boiling point would be lower or higher than that of the alcohol with the same number of carbon atoms.

_____

_____

3. The following questions apply to the compound labeled B on the transparency.

   a. What is the name of the compound? _____

   b. To what category of organic compound does it belong? _____

   c. State whether you would expect this compound to be polar, and whether it can form hydrogen bonds with water.

_____

4. The following questions apply to the compound labeled C on the transparency.

   a. What is the name of the compound? _____

   b. To what category of organic compound does it belong? _____

   c. What are the name and formula of the functional group of compounds in this category?

_____

   d. State whether you would expect this compound to be polar, whether it would ionize in water, and what the color of litmus paper in the resulting solution would be.

_____

_____

5. What is the name of the ion labeled D? _____

6. What are the names of the compounds labeled E and F on the transparency?

_____

Name _____   Date _____   Class _____

Kinds of Organic Reactions

Use with Chapter 23, Section 23.4

A $H\!-\!\overset{\displaystyle H}{\underset{\displaystyle I}{C}}\!-\!\overset{\displaystyle H}{\underset{\displaystyle I}{C}}\!-\!H \;\rightarrow\; \overset{H}{\underset{H}{}}C\!=\!C\overset{H}{\underset{H}{}} \;+\; I\!-\!I$

B $\overset{H}{\underset{H}{}}C\!=\!C\overset{H}{\underset{H}{}} \;+\; \overset{O}{\underset{H\quad H}{}} \;\rightarrow\; H\!-\!\overset{H}{\underset{H}{C}}\!-\!\overset{H}{\underset{O-H}{C}}\!-\!H$

C $H\!-\!\overset{\displaystyle O}{\underset{\displaystyle O-H}{C}} \;+\; \overset{H}{\underset{H}{O-C-H}} \;\rightarrow\; H\!-\!\overset{\displaystyle O}{C}\overset{H}{\underset{\underset{H}{O-C-H}}{}} \;+\; \overset{O}{\underset{H\quad H}{}}$

D $H\!-\!\overset{H}{\underset{H}{C}}\!-\!\overset{H}{\underset{H}{C}}\!-\!H \;\rightarrow\; \overset{H}{\underset{H}{}}C\!=\!C\overset{H}{\underset{H}{}} \;+\; H\!-\!H$

E $\overset{H}{\underset{H\;\;H\;\;Cl}{C}} \;+\; [O\!-\!H]^{-} \;\rightarrow\; \overset{H}{\underset{H\;\;H\;\;O-H}{C}} \;+\; Cl^{-}$

F $\overset{H}{\underset{H}{}}C\!=\!C\overset{H}{\underset{H}{}} \;+\; H\!-\!H \;\rightarrow\; H\!-\!\overset{H}{\underset{H}{C}}\!-\!\overset{H}{\underset{H}{C}}\!-\!H$

G $\overset{H}{\underset{H}{}}C\!=\!C\overset{H}{\underset{H}{}} \;+\; F\!-\!F \;\rightarrow\; H\!-\!\overset{F}{\underset{H}{C}}\!-\!\overset{F}{\underset{H}{C}}\!-\!H$

H $H\!-\!\overset{H}{\underset{H}{C}}\!-\!\overset{H}{\underset{O-H}{C}}\!-\!H \;\rightarrow\; \overset{H}{\underset{H}{}}C\!=\!C\overset{H}{\underset{H}{}} \;+\; \overset{O}{\underset{H\quad H}{}}$

I $\overset{H}{\underset{H\;\;H}{C}} \;+\; Br\!-\!Br \;\rightarrow\; \overset{H}{\underset{H\;\;Br}{C}} \;+\; H\!-\!Br$

TEACHING TRANSPARENCY WORKSHEET

(71)

Kinds of Organic Reactions

Use with Chapter 23, Section 23.4

1. What is the name for the category of reaction in which one atom or a group of atoms in a molecule is replaced by another?

_____

2. Which two of the reactions labeled A–I are examples of that type of reaction?

_____

3. Which of these two reactions is also a halogenation reaction?

_____

4. What is the name for the category of reaction in which atoms on two adjacent carbon atoms are removed, forming an additional bond between the carbon atoms?

_____

5. Which three of the reactions labeled A–I are examples of that type of reaction?

_____

6. Which of these three reactions is also a dehydration reaction?

_____

7. Which of these three reactions is also a dehydrogenation reaction?

_____

8. What is the name for the category of reaction in which other atoms bond to each of two double-bonded or triple-bonded atoms?

_____

9. Which three of the reactions labeled A–I are examples of that type of reaction?

_____

10. Which of these three reactions is also a hydration reaction?

_____

11. Which of these three reactions is also a hydrogenation reaction?

_____

12. What is the name for the category of reaction in which two smaller organic molecules combine to form a more complex molecule, accompanied by the loss of a small molecule such as water?

_____

13. Which of the reactions labeled A–I is an example of that type of reaction?

_____

TEACHING TRANSPARENCY MASTER (72)

Forming Polymers

**Use with Chapter 23,
Section 23.5**

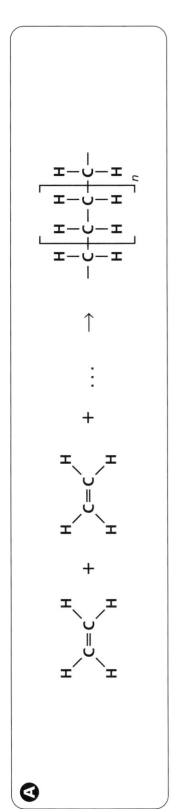

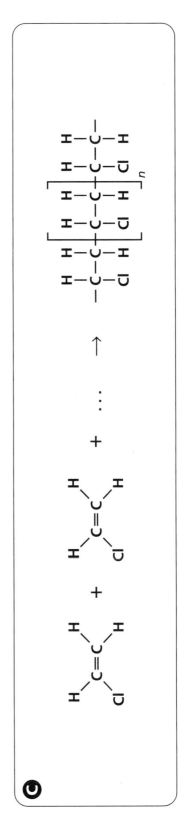

Forming Polymers

1. Define the following terms.

  a. polymer

  _____

  b. monomer

  _____

  c. structural unit of a polymer

  _____

2. Look at the reaction labeled A, which illustrates a polymerization reaction.

  a. What are the name and formula of the monomer? _____

  b. What does the structure labeled *n* in reaction A represent?

  _____

  c. What is the name of the polymer produced? _____

  d. What kind of polymerization reaction is reaction A: condensation or addition? How
  can you tell?

  _____

3. Look at polymerization reaction B.

  a. The first of the monomers shown is called methyl terephthalate. What is the name of
  the second monomer?

  _____

  b. What does the structure labeled *n* in reaction B represent?

  _____

  c. The name of the polymer produced in reaction B is poly(ethylene terephthalate). It is
  commonly known as Dacron. What is the name of the other product formed?

  _____

  d. What kind of polymerization reaction is reaction B: condensation or addition? How
  can you tell?

  _____

4. Look at polymerization reaction C.

  a. The monomer is commonly called vinyl chloride. What is its more formal
  chemical name?

  _____

  b. The common abbreviated name of the polymer produced in reaction C is PVC. Of
  what complete name is PVC an abbreviation?

  _____

TEACHING TRANSPARENCY MASTER

73

Enzymes

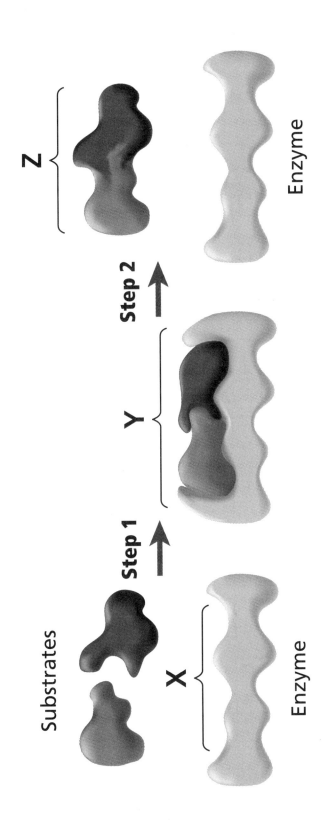

Name ______________________ Date ____________ Class ____________

TEACHING TRANSPARENCY WORKSHEET 73

Enzymes

Use with Chapter 24, Section 24.1

1. What is the area labeled X called?

____

2. What is Y?

____

3. What is Z?

____

4. Explain what is happening at each step in the diagram.

Step 1 ____

____

Step 2 ____

____

5. Compare the shape of the enzyme at the beginning and at the end of the reaction.

____

6. What effect do enzymes have on the following?

a. reaction rate ____

b. activation energy ____

7. How does the large size of enzyme molecules affect their ability to catalyze reactions?

____

____

____

____

8. What reaction does the enzyme papain catalyze?

____

____

9. Name and describe three functions of proteins in addition to their role as enzymes.

____

____

____

____

Name _____ Date _____ Class _____

Condensation Reactions

Use with Chapter 24, Sections 24.1–24.3

1

$$
\begin{array}{c}
\underset{\underset{\text{A}}{\underbrace{\quad\quad\quad}}}{\overset{H}{\underset{H}{N}}-\overset{R_1}{\underset{H}{C}}-\overset{}{\underset{O}{C}}-OH}
\;+\;
\underset{}{\overset{H}{\underset{H}{N}}-\overset{R_2}{\underset{H}{C}}-\overset{}{\underset{O}{C}}-OH}
\;\rightarrow\;
\underset{\underset{\text{B}}{\underbrace{\quad\quad\quad\quad\quad\quad}}}{\overset{H}{\underset{H}{N}}-\overset{R_1}{\underset{H}{C}}-\overset{}{\underset{O}{C}}-\overset{H}{N}-\overset{R_2}{\underset{H}{C}}-\overset{}{\underset{O}{C}}-OH}
\;+\;H_2O
\end{array}
$$

2

3

TEACHING TRANSPARENCY WORKSHEET   **74**

Condensation Reactions

**Use with Chapter 24,
Sections 24.1–24.3**

1. Identify the type of organic compound represented by each of the letters A–F on the transparency.

A _____   D _____

B _____   E _____

C _____   F _____

2. What functional group is represented by the bond that is formed in reaction 1?

_____

3. Where does the water that is formed in reaction 1 come from?

_____

_____

_____

4. In reaction 1, is the order in which the two reactants are linked important? Explain.

_____

_____

_____

5. What functional group is represented by the bond that is formed in reaction 2?

_____

6. What is the common name of the three-carbon molecule that reacts with the compounds labeled E in reaction 3?

_____

7. What functional group is represented by the bonds that are formed in reaction 3?

_____

8. Contrast the water-solubility of reaction products D and F. Explain the difference.

_____

_____

_____

_____

_____

TEACHING TRANSPARENCY MASTER

75

Photosynthesis, Cellular Respiration, and Fermentation

Use with Chapter 24, Section 24.5

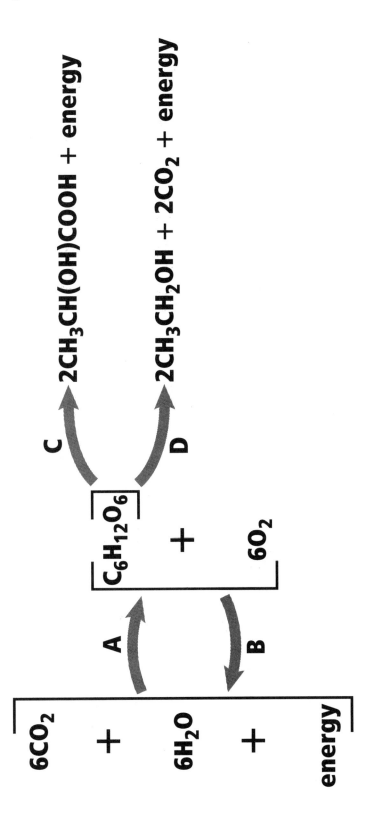

Name ______________________ Date ____________ Class ____________

TEACHING TRANSPARENCY WORKSHEET **75**

Photosynthesis, Cellular Respiration, and Fermentation

Use with Chapter 24, Section 24.5

1. Identify the metabolic processes labeled A–D on the transparency.

A ______________________ **C** ______________________

B ______________________ **D** ______________________

2. What kinds of organisms carry out each metabolic process?

A ______________________

B ______________________

C ______________________

D ______________________

3. Label each metabolic process as anabolism or catabolism.

A ______________________ **C** ______________________

B ______________________ **D** ______________________

4. Identify the following compounds shown on the transparency.

$C_6H_{12}O_6$ ______________________

$CH_3CH(OH)COOH$ ______________________

CH_3CH_2OH ______________________

5. What provides the energy that is used in process A? ______________________

6. Compare the efficiencies of processes B, C, and D in terms of ATP production.

____

____

____

7. Explain how process C is related to some instances of muscle pain and fatigue.

____

____

____

8. Describe three commercial applications of process D.

____

____

Production of Transuranium Elements

Use with Chapter 25,
Section 25.3

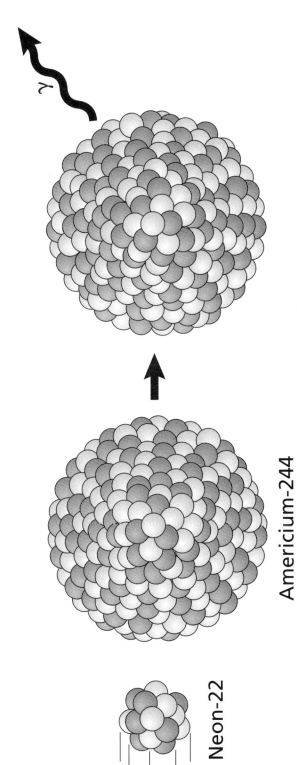

γ

Americium-244

Neon-22

Isotope	Half-Life	Decay Mode
Americium-244	10 hours	Alpha emission
Dubnium-263	30 seconds	Beta emission
Lawrencium-262	3.6 hours	Electron capture
Seaborgium-266	~ 20 seconds	Alpha emission

Name ______________________ Date ____________ Class ____________

TEACHING TRANSPARENCY WORKSHEET **76**

Production of Transuranium Elements

Use with Chapter 25, Section 25.3

1. Does the diagram illustrate a natural transmutation reaction or an induced transmutation reaction?

____

2. What is the name and nuclear symbol of the isotope produced in the reaction?

____

3. What difficulties do you foresee in trying to carry out the reaction shown here?

____

____

____

____

4. Write a nuclear equation to show how dubnium-263, lawrencium-262, and seaborgium-266 can be produced from a nuclear reaction of neon-22 and americium-224.

____

____

____

5. Each of the radioisotopes in the table decays within 20 seconds to 10 hours. Write a nuclear equation for each decay.

____

____

____

____

6. Which, if any, of the four isotopes listed in the table would you expect to find at Earth's surface? Why?

____

____

____

TEACHING TRANSPARENCY MASTER   **77**

Formation of Ozone

Use with Chapter 26,
Section 26.1

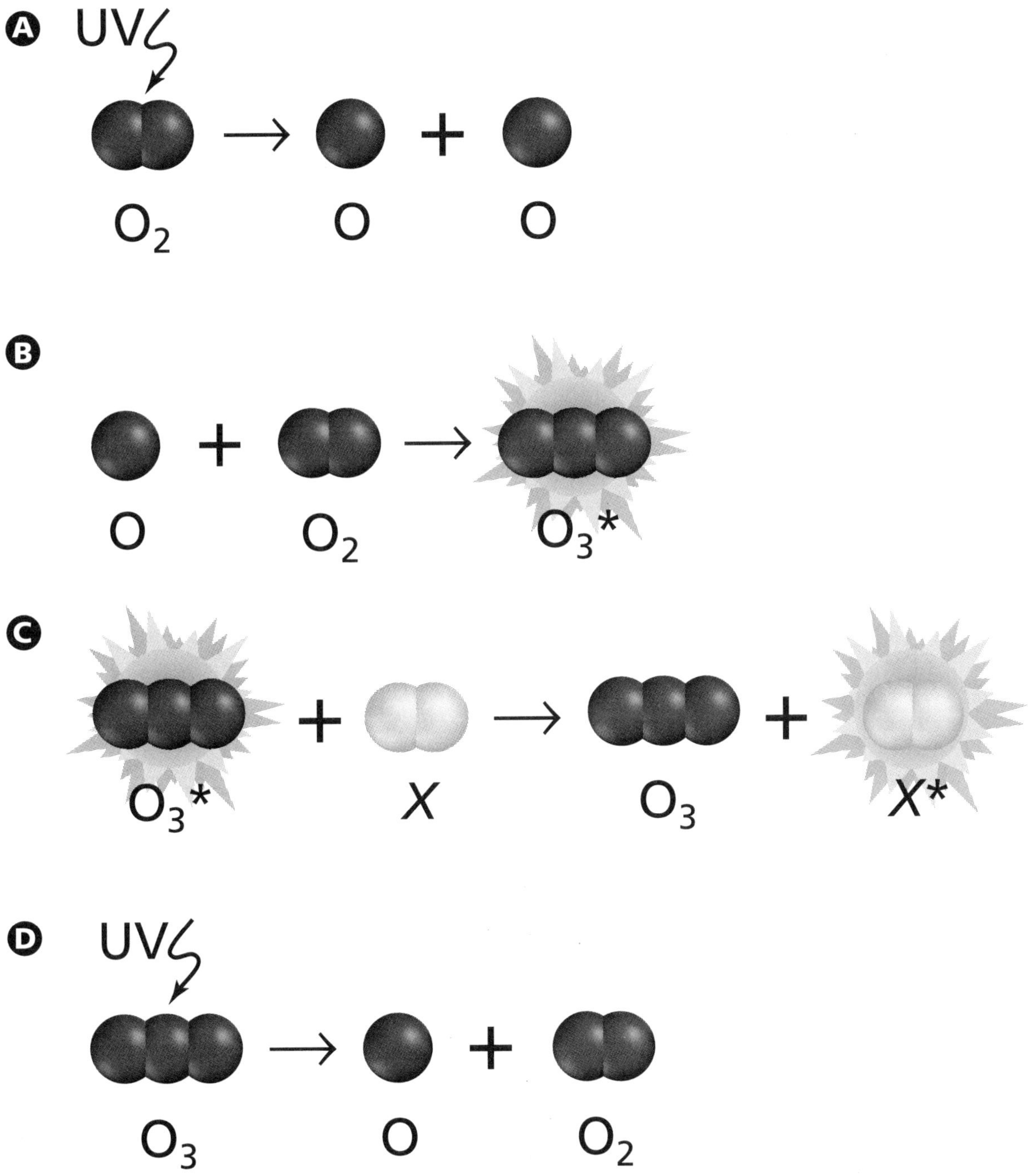

A UV

$$O_2 \rightarrow O + O$$

B

$$O + O_2 \rightarrow O_3^*$$

C

$$O_3^* + X \rightarrow O_3 + X^*$$

D UV

$$O_3 \rightarrow O + O_2$$

Name ______________________ Date ____________ Class ____________

TEACHING TRANSPARENCY WORKSHEET 77

Formation of Ozone

Use with Chapter 26, Section 26.1

1. What is the source of energy used in the decomposition of the oxygen molecule in step A of this reaction?

____

2. Why does this step of the reaction take place in the stratosphere but not in higher layers of the atmosphere?

____

3. Why does this step of the reaction not take place in the troposphere?

____

4. What do the asterisks on the molecule indicate?

____

5. Why is the ozone molecule formed in step B of the reaction said to be energized?

____

6. Name two natural components of the atmosphere represented by the symbol *X* in step C of this reaction.

____

7. What process is responsible for the reactions shown in steps A and D?

____

8. Of what importance, if any, is this series of reactions for life on Earth?

____

____

TEACHING TRANSPARENCY MASTER

The Water Cycle

**Use with Chapter 26,
Section 26.2**

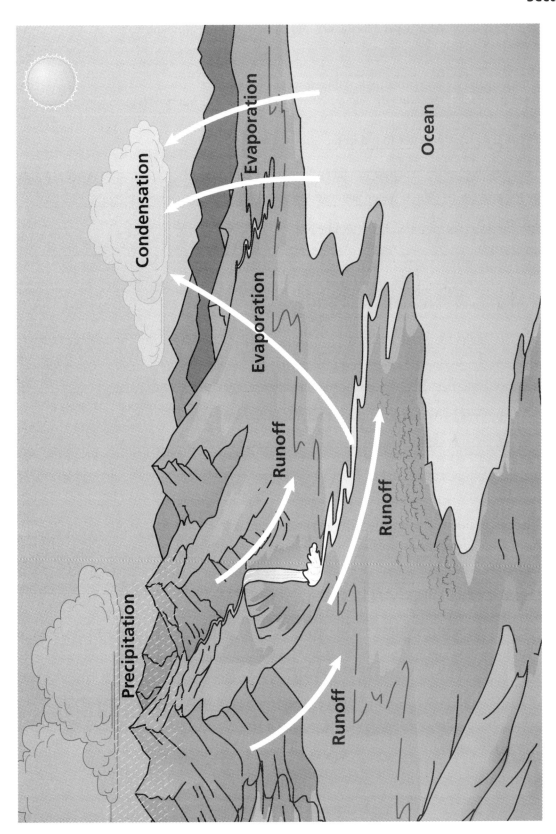

Name _____ Date _____ Class _____

The Water Cycle

**Use with Chapter 26,
Section 26.2**

1. By what process does water move from lakes and oceans into the atmosphere?

_____

2. What is the source of energy that makes this process possible?

_____

3. In what physical states is water found in the atmosphere?

_____

4. Describe the process by which water vapor in the atmosphere becomes precipitation.

_____

_____

_____

5. Describe what happens to water that falls to Earth's surface as rain.

_____

_____

_____

6. Describe the process by which groundwater returns to the atmosphere.

_____

_____

_____

7. How is the composition of groundwater, water vapor, and water in the oceans different?

_____

_____

_____

The Carbon Cycle

**Use with Chapter 26,
Section 26.4**

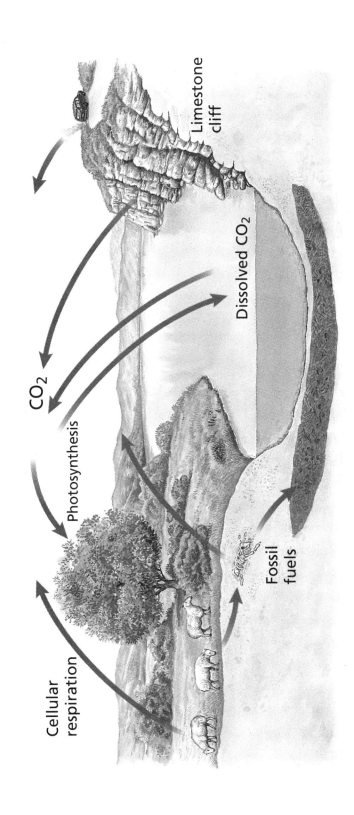

Limestone cliff

Dissolved CO_2

CO_2

Photosynthesis

Fossil fuels

Cellular respiration

TEACHING TRANSPARENCY WORKSHEET

The Carbon Cycle

**Use with Chapter 26,
Section 26.4**

1. By what natural processes does carbon dioxide enter Earth's atmosphere?

_____

_____

2. How do human activities affect the amount of carbon dioxide in the atmosphere?

_____

_____

3. By what natural processes is carbon dioxide removed from Earth's atmosphere?

_____

4. Some carbon is stored in the lithosphere for millions of years. In what forms is it stored and how does it get there?

_____

_____

_____

5. What role do green plants play in the carbon cycle?

_____

_____

_____

6. What role do animals play in the carbon cycle?

_____

_____

_____

7. What role do marine animals play in the carbon cycle?

_____

_____

_____

_____

TEACHING TRANSPARENCY MASTER

80

The Nitrogen Cycle

Use with Chapter 26,
Section 26.4

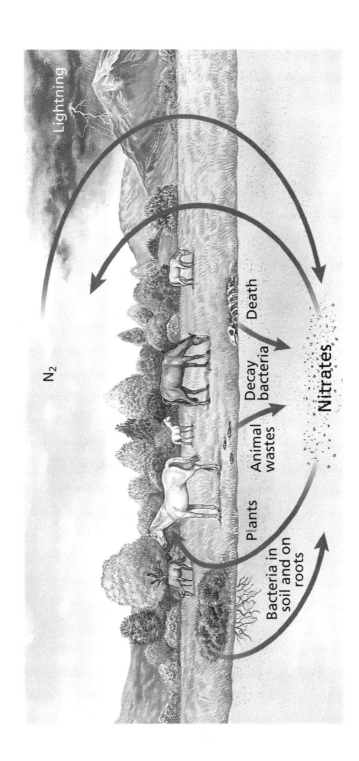

TEACHING TRANSPARENCY WORKSHEET **80**

The Nitrogen Cycle

**Use with Chapter 26,
Section 26.4**

1. What does the term *nitrogen fixation* mean?

_____

_____

2. What role does lightning play in the nitrogen cycle? Write the equations that show this.

_____

_____

3. What role does rain water play in the nitrogen cycle?

_____

4. What role do soil bacteria play in the nitrogen cycle?

_____

_____

5. In what form does nitrogen most commonly occur in the atmosphere?

_____

6. In what form do green plants take nitrogen from the soil?

_____

7. In what form and from what source do animals get nitrogen?

_____

8. How is nitrogen recycled from living organisms to the atmosphere?

_____

_____

TEACHING TRANSPARENCY WORKSHEETS

Answer Key

TEACHING TRANSPARENCY WORKSHEET

2

A Scientific Method

Use with Chapter 1,
Section 1.3

1. Define the term *scientific method*.
   A scientific method is a systematic, organized approach used in all scientific study
   to do research and verify the work of others.

2. What is typically the first step in a scientific method? Give two examples.
   Making observations; examples include any information gathered by using the
   five senses or by making measurements.

3. What is a hypothesis?
   Answers should include that a hypothesis is a testable, tentative statement of
   explanation for observations.

4. Compare and contrast a hypothesis and a theory.
   Both are tentative explanations of scientific phenomena, subject to revision
   based on new data. However, a theory is supported by many experiments and
   lines of evidence.

5. Distinguish between an independent variable and a dependent variable.
   An independent variable is a variable that is controlled by the experimenter.
   The dependent variable is the variable that may change in response to the
   changes in the independent variable.

6. Suppose you observe that tadpoles hatched in stagnant water have a lower rate of survival
   than tadpoles hatched in water that is churned and aerated. Write a possible hypothesis
   you might test based on your observations. How might you test your hypothesis?
   Answers will vary. One possible hypothesis is that the stagnant water kills
   tadpoles. One way to test the hypothesis is to raise tadpoles in aquariums that
   have different levels of aeration.

7. You notice that when salt is sprinkled on an icy sidewalk, the ice melts even when the
   temperature is below freezing. Write a possible hypothesis you might test based on your
   observation. How might you test your hypothesis?
   Answers will vary. One possible hypothesis is that the salt lowers the freezing
   point of water. One way to test the hypothesis is to compare the temperatures at
   which ice freezes with salt and without salt.

4   Chemistry: Matter and Change • Chapter 1   Teaching Transparency Worksheets

---

TEACHING TRANSPARENCY WORKSHEET

1

Earth's Atmosphere

Use with Chapter 1,
Section 1.1

1. In which layer of Earth's atmosphere do commercial airplanes fly?
   the troposphere

2. In which layer of Earth's atmosphere would you find the peaks of mountains?
   the troposphere

3. In which layer of Earth's atmosphere would you find the ozone layer?
   the stratosphere

4. In which layer of Earth's atmosphere would you find the air you breathe?
   the troposphere

5. In which layer of Earth's atmosphere does ozone form? Explain how it forms.
   Ozone forms in the stratosphere when oxygen gas is struck by ultraviolet
   radiation. The energy from the radiation breaks apart the gas molecules,
   which then can interact to form ozone.

6. Over which region(s) of Earth are the highest concentrations of ozone found? Over which
   region(s) of Earth are the lowest concentrations of ozone found?
   The highest concentrations of ozone are found over the equator. The lowest
   concentrations are found over the north and south poles.

7. What is the source for the ultraviolet radiation in Earth's atmosphere?
   the Sun

8. How does ultraviolet radiation affect Earth's surface?
   Ultraviolet radiation helps to warm Earth's surface.

9. How does ultraviolet radiation affect humans and other organisms?
   Answers will vary. Ultraviolet radiation can cause sunburn, skin cancer, and
   cataracts in humans. It can also harm plants and animals, affecting the food
   supply.

10. How does the ozone layer protect Earth from ultraviolet radiation?
    The ozone layer absorbs much of the ultraviolet radiation before it reaches
    Earth's surface.

2   Chemistry: Matter and Change • Chapter 1   Teaching Transparency Worksheets

---

Name _____ Date _____ Class _____

TEACHING TRANSPARENCY WORKSHEET ③

Laboratory Safety

Use with Chapter 1, Section 1.4

1. What should you do before entering the lab? List at least three things.
   Answers may include any of the following: read the entire lab assignment, read all caution statements, review all safety symbols, ask the teacher questions if necessary, dress appropriately, tie back long hair, and remove contact lenses.

2. What should you do if a chemical comes in contact with your skin?
   Flush the area immediately with large quantities of cool, running water and inform the teacher of the incident.

3. When should you read the label on a chemical container?
   The label should be read three times: before picking up the container, while holding the container, and when putting the container back.

4. What is the proper way to prepare an acid solution?
   Always add the acid slowly to water.

5. When should you wear safety goggles? Gloves?
   Safety goggles should be worn whenever a person is working in the lab. Gloves should be worn when chemicals are used that cause irritations or can be absorbed through the skin.

6. What kind of clothing should NOT be worn in the lab?
   Very loose-fitting clothes, long sleeves, open-toed shoes, and dangling jewelry should not be worn in the lab.

7. What should you do when you have completed an assignment in the lab?
   Clean and put away all equipment, clean the work area, make sure the gas and water faucets are turned off, and wash your hands with soap and water.

6   Chemistry: Matter and Change • Chapter 1   Teaching Transparency Worksheets

---

Name _____ Date _____ Class _____

TEACHING TRANSPARENCY WORKSHEET ④

Converting Units

Use with Chapter 2, Section 2.2

Exchange rates fluctuate daily. The ones shown on the transparency are for July 15, 2000. Show your work when necessary.

1. How much does the portable radio cassette player cost in U.S. dollars?
   Students should use any of the conversions shown to calculate that the item costs $85.

2. Which currency listed is closest to the value of the U.S. dollar?
   At 1.06 per dollar, the euro is closest in value to that of the U.S. dollar.

3. Assume that you have only British pounds. How many pounds would the portable radio cassette player cost? Show your work.
   £56.10. $85 multiplied by 0.66 pounds/dollar = £56.10.

4. While traveling in Germany and France, you buy ice cream cones. The French cones sell for 10 French francs. The German cones sell for 1.25 German marks. Which cone costs you more U.S. dollars?
   10 FF divided by 6.98 FF/dollar = $1.43. 1.25 DM (German marks) divided by 2.07 DM/dollar = $0.60. Therefore, the French cone costs more U.S. dollars.

Suppose on January 15, 2001, the exchange rates have changed as shown to the right. Use these exchange rates to answer questions 5 and 6. Show your work when necessary.

Exchange Rates	
Country	**Currency units per U.S. dollar**
Belgium	42.95
Britain	0.71
Canada	1.37
France	6.51
Germany	2.09
Italy	2,085
Switzerland	1.61
Euro	1.02

5. A video game costs 570 French francs on January 15, 2001. What is its price in U.S. dollars? Has the price risen or dropped since July 15, 2000?
   The game costs slightly more today than it would have six months ago. 570 FF divided by 6.51 FF/dollar = $87.56.

6. A department store has stores in both Germany and in Switzerland. A Swiss shopper pays 12 Swiss francs for a candle. A German shopper pays 12 German marks for the identical candle.

   a. Which shopper gets the better deal?
   The German shopper gets the better deal. 12 SF divided by 1.61 SF/dollar = $7.45 and 12 DM divided by 2.09 DM/dollar = $5.74.

   b. What is the advantage of using the euro in both Germany and Switzerland?
   If the price is in euros, then the cost is the same for each shopper.

8   Chemistry: Matter and Change • Chapter 2   Teaching Transparency Worksheets

TEACHING TRANSPARENCY WORKSHEET 5

Precision and Accuracy

In golf, a player tries to use the fewest swings, or strokes, of a club to hit a ball into a series of holes. The player keeps score by counting the number of strokes used for each hole. The player's final score is the total number of strokes. The lower the number of strokes used, the better the score.

Par is a term that refers to the target score for a particular hole. It is the number of strokes that a player is expected to use to hit the ball into that hole. A player's accuracy is related to how closely his or her score comes to par. The closer a player's score is to par, the more accurate the player. A player's precision refers to the consistency of his or her score in comparison with par. A player whose score deviates consistently from par at each hole is more precise than one whose score deviates inconsistently.

1. Which player's overall game was most accurate?
   Shekegi's game was most accurate.

2. Which player's overall game was both accurate and precise?
   Anne-Marie's game was most accurate and precise.

3. Use the terms *accurate* and *precise* to describe Marguerite's overall game.
   Marguerite's game is precise, but not accurate.

4. Which player seems to be neither accurate nor precise in his or her golf play?
   Jon is neither accurate nor precise in his golf game.

5. At the end of a golf game, which is more important: precision or accuracy? Explain your answer.
   Accept all supported answers. Students may say that accuracy is more important because it determines the winner. Students may say that precision is more important because it is a better gauge of a player's skill and a better predictor of his or her performance on future games.

6. Compare and contrast the results of a golf game to the data from an experiment.
   Answers will vary. Students should recognize the similarity between accepted value in an experiment and par in golf. They should note, however, that in golf, variables are not held constant as they are in experiments. Also, the way in which data are produced in multiple experimental trials does not vary, whereas the way in which the results of a golf game are reached does vary.

TEACHING TRANSPARENCY WORKSHEET 6

Interpreting Graphs

1. What kind of graph is this?
   It is a bar graph.

2. What variables are compared in the graph?
   The graph compares sound quality and price for different brands of speakers.

3. Which product has the best sound quality? Which has the poorest sound quality?
   Magnasound has the best sound quality. Wal's Best has the worst.

4. Which product costs the most? The least?
   Wolfvox costs the most. Wal's Best costs the least.

5. If there are no limits on the amount of money you can spend, which product would you buy? Why?
   Accept all answers that are supported by the data. Students might choose Magnasound because it has the best sound quality.

6. If you can spend only $120, which product would you buy? Why?
   Accept all answers that are supported by the data. Students might choose Thoreau because it has the best sound quality for the given price.

7. If you can spend up to $200, which product would you buy? Why?
   Accept all answers that are supported by the data. Students might choose Hi-technic because it has the best sound quality below $200. The only product with (slightly) better sound quality costs more than $200.

8. Which product is the best deal? Which is the worst deal?
   Accept all answers that are supported by the data. Students might say that Thoreau is the best deal because it has the highest sound quality per dollar. Others might say that Hi-technic is the best deal because it offers almost the highest sound quality of all the products, but at a lower price than Magnasound. Students might suggest that Wolfvox is the worst deal because it costs the most, but has only average sound quality. There are products with better sound quality available at a lower price.

TEACHING TRANSPARENCY WORKSHEET 7

Use with Chapter 3, Section 3.1

States of Matter

1. Name the physical states in which almost all matter exists.
   solid, liquid, gas

2. In which state(s) of matter are the molecules most compressed?
   solid

3. In which state(s) of matter do the molecules fill the entire volume of a container?
   gas

4. In which state(s) does matter take the shape of a container?
   liquid and gas

5. Compare the distance between the molecules of a gas in a very small container with the distance between the molecules of the same gas in a very large container. Explain your answer.
   The gas molecules will be spaced farther apart in a large container than in a small container because the molecules in a gas spread out to fill the entire volume of a container.

6. What happens to the volume of a liquid when it is poured from a small container into a large container?
   The liquid's volume remains the same, regardless of the size of the container.

7. Suppose you fill a glass with ice cubes. When the ice cubes melt, is the glass still full? Explain your answer.
   When the ice cubes melt, the resulting liquid water will not fill the glass because there were air spaces within the ice cubes. The liquid will conform to the shape of the container and fill it only partially.

8. Suppose you fill a container with steam and then seal the container. When the steam in the container changes to liquid water at room temperature, will the container still be full? Explain your answer.
   The liquid water will not fill the container because the molecules of the liquid will be much closer together than the molecules of the steam were.

TEACHING TRANSPARENCY WORKSHEET 8

Use with Chapter 3, Sections 3.2

Conservation of Mass

1. What happens when mercury(II) oxide is heated?
   A chemical reaction occurs in which mercury(II) oxide becomes liquid mercury and oxygen gas.

2. What does the law of conservation of mass state?
   Mass is neither created nor destroyed in any process.

3. Write the law of conservation of mass in mathematical terms.
   $Mass_{reactants} = Mass_{products}$

4. Assume that the test tube shown in the transparency started out having 15.00 g of mercury(II) oxide. After heating the test tube, you find no mercury(II) oxide left and 1.11 g of oxygen gas. What mass of liquid mercury was produced by the chemical reaction? Show your work.
   $Mass_{reactants} = Mass_{products}$
   $Mass_{mercury(II) oxide} = Mass_{mercury} + Mass_{oxygen}$
   $15.00 g = Mass_{mercury} + 1.11 g$
   $Mass_{mercury} = 13.89 g$

5. Assume that the test tube shown started out having 10.00 g of mercury(II) oxide. After heating the test tube briefly, you find 1.35 g mercury(II) oxide left and 8.00 g of liquid mercury. How much oxygen gas was produced by the chemical reaction? Show your work.
   $Mass_{reactants} = Mass_{products}$
   $Mass_{mercury(II) oxide}$ used in the reaction $= Mass_{mercury} + Mass_{oxygen}$
   $10.00 g - 1.35 g = 8.00 g + Mass_{oxygen}$
   $Mass_{oxygen} = 0.65 g$

6. Suppose you heat some mercury(II) oxide in a test tube similar to the one shown. After the chemical reaction, you find 12.5 g of liquid mercury and 1.0 g of oxygen gas. There is no mercury(II) oxide left in the test tube. How much mercury(II) oxide did you start with? Show your work.
   $Mass_{reactants} = Mass_{products}$
   $Mass_{mercury(II) oxide} = Mass_{mercury} + Mass_{oxygen}$
   $Mass_{mercury(II) oxide} = 12.5 g + 1.0 g$
   $Mass_{mercury(II) oxide} = 13.5 g$

Teaching Transparency Worksheets Answer Key   Chemistry: Matter and Change   **T165**

TEACHING TRANSPARENCY WORKSHEET

9

Types of Matter

Use with Chapter 3,
Section 3.4

1. Into what two broad classes can all matter be divided?
   mixtures and pure substances

2. What is the difference between a mixture and a pure substance?
   A mixture can be separated into its component substances by physical means;
   however, a pure substance cannot.

3. What is the difference between a compound and an element?
   A compound can be broken down chemically into smaller substances; however, an
   element cannot.

4. Can a compound be a heterogeneous mixture? Explain your answer by referring to the diagram.
   No; according to the diagram, a heterogeneous mixture can be separated into its
   components by physical means. A compound cannot be separated into
   its components by physical means.

5. A list of compounds and elements is given below. Circle the substances that are elements.

   (aluminum)   water
   gold   (oxygen)   (platinum)
   sugar   (chlorine)   brass
   salt

6. How can you tell the difference between a homogeneous mixture and a heterogeneous mixture?
   A homogeneous mixture has a uniform composition, whereas a heterogeneous
   mixture does not. Thus, if you can see the different components in a mixture,
   then it is a heterogeneous mixture.

7. Label each mixture below as either homogeneous or heterogeneous.
   a. air **homogeneous**   e. finger paint **homogeneous**
   b. clay **heterogeneous**   f. vinegar **homogeneous**
   c. homemade lemonade (with pulp) **heterogeneous**   g. soil **heterogeneous**
   d. oatmeal raisin cookie **heterogeneous**

8. List three methods that are commonly used to separate mixtures into their component substances.
   Separation methods include filtration, distillation, crystallization, and
   chromatography.

TEACHING TRANSPARENCY WORKSHEET

10

Mass Percentage and the
Law of Definite Proportions

Use with Chapter 3,
Section 3.4

1. Suppose you analyze the composition of an unnamed compound. Your analysis shows that the compound is 51.30% oxygen, 42.20% carbon, and 6.50% hydrogen by mass. What can you conclude about the compound?
   It is sucrose.

2. What is the mass percentage of carbon in 5.000 g of sucrose? 50.00 g of sucrose? 500.0 g of sucrose? Explain.
   42.20%; the mass percentage of carbon is consistent regardless of the amount of
   sucrose; this is the law of definite proportions.

3. How many grams of oxygen are in 50.00 g of sucrose? Show your work.
   mass percentage of oxygen = mass of oxygen/mass of sucrose × 100%
   51.30% = mass of oxygen/50.00 g × 100%
   mass of oxygen = 51.30% × 50.00 g/100% = 25.65 g

4. How many grams of carbon are in 100.0 g of sucrose? Show your work.
   mass percentage of carbon = mass of carbon/mass of sucrose × 100%
   42.20% = mass of carbon/100.0 g × 100%
   mass of carbon = 42.20% × 100.0 g/100% = 42.20 g

5. How many grams of hydrogen are in 6.0 g of sucrose? Show your work.
   mass percentage of hydrogen = mass of hydrogen/mass of sucrose × 100%
   6.50% = mass of hydrogen/6.0 g × 100%
   mass of hydrogen = 6.50% × 6.0 g/100% = 0.39 g

7. A 20.00-g sample of ordinary table salt contains 12.13 g of chlorine and 7.87 g of sodium. Calculate the mass percentage of each element in salt.
   mass percentage of an element (%) = mass of element/mass of compound × 100%
   mass percentage of chlorine = 12.13 g/20.00 g × 100% = 60.65%
   mass percentage of sodium = 7.87 g/20.00 g × 100% = 39.35%

8. Draw a circle graph to represent your answer to question 7.
   Students should show a circle graph divided into two wedges: one representing
   approximately 60% of the circle and one representing approximately 40% of
   the circle.

TEACHING TRANSPARENCY WORKSHEET

12

Use with Chapter 4,
Section 4.2

Understanding Rutherford's Gold Foil Experiment

1. What kind of particles do the arrows represent? What is the charge of the particles?
The arrows represent alpha particles, which have a positive (2+) charge.

2. Which diagram depicts the plum pudding model of an atom?
diagram A

3. Which diagram depicts Rutherford's actual results from his gold foil experiment? How did the actual results differ from the expected results?
diagram B; some of the alpha particles were deflected at large angles.

4. What did Rutherford conclude from the results of his experiment?
Rutherford concluded that the plum pudding model of the atom was incorrect. He also concluded that an atom is made mostly of empty space with a tiny, dense, centrally located nucleus that is positively charged and contains almost all of the atom's mass.

5. Explain why Rutherford expected the alpha particles to pass through the plum pudding model of the atom with little or no deflection.
The massive alpha particles were expected to be largely unaffected by the much less massive electrons. The weak, diffusely distributed positive charge inside the atom was also not expected to affect the positively charged alpha particles.

TEACHING TRANSPARENCY WORKSHEET

11

Use with Chapter 4,
Section 4.2

Cathode Ray Experiments

1. What is a cathode ray?
A cathode ray is a beam of negatively charged particles or electrons.

2. What do the experiments in A, B, and C have in common?
Answers may vary. All three experiments have a voltage source, a cathode, an anode, gas at low pressure, and a phosphor that allows the position of the cathode ray to be determined.

3. Examine the cathode ray experiment in A. Describe the path of the cathode ray from its origin to its termination.
The cathode ray travels from the cathode toward the anode, passing through the hole in the anode and traveling in a straight line through the tube, where it strikes the phosphor screen.

4. Compare the experimental setup in B with the setup in C. How do the two setups differ? What do both experiments show in terms of the cathode ray's charge?
In B, the cathode ray passes through a magnetic field, whereas in C, the cathode ray passes between two electrically charged plates. Both experiments show that the cathode ray is made of charged particles.

5. Examine the cathode ray experiment in B. What does this experiment show?
The experiment shows that the cathode ray consists of charged particles that are affected by a magnetic field.

6. Examine the cathode ray experiment in C. Explain why the cathode ray bends.
The negatively charged cathode ray bends toward the positively charged plate due to electrical forces of attraction.

Name _____ Date _____ Class _____

TEACHING TRANSPARENCY WORKSHEET   **13**

Isotopes

Use with Chapter 4,
Section 4.3

1. What do the following symbols represent?

    a. e^- _____ electron

    b. n^0 _____ neutron

    c. p^+ _____ proton

2. Which subatomic particles are found in an atom's nucleus?
    Protons and neutrons are in the nucleus.

3. Which subatomic particle identifies an atom as that of a particular element?
    The number of protons in an atom identify the atom as a particular element.

4. Explain why atoms are neutral even though they contain charged particles.
    The protons and electrons in an atom have opposite charges and are equal in number. Because of this, the net charge on an atom is zero.

5. What do the numbers 39, 40, and 41 after the element name potassium refer to?
    The numbers refer to the mass number—the sum of protons and neutrons in each atom's nucleus. They are an approximate value of each atom's mass.

6. Write the symbolic notation for each of the following isotopes.

    a. potassium-39 _____ $^{39}_{19}K$

    b. potassium-40 _____ $^{40}_{19}K$

    c. potassium-41 _____ $^{41}_{19}K$

7. Write an equation showing the relationship between an atom's atomic number and its mass number.
    Mass number = atomic number + number of neutrons

8. Lithium has two isotopes: lithium-6 and lithium-7. Draw a diagram, like those shown on the transparency, for each lithium isotope. Label the protons, electrons, neutrons, and electron cloud in each diagram.
    Students should draw two atomic nuclei, each surrounded by an electron cloud. Both atoms should have three protons in the nucleus and three electrons in the electron cloud. One of the atoms should have three neutrons in the nucleus; the other should have four neutrons in the nucleus.

Name _____ Date _____ Class _____

TEACHING TRANSPARENCY WORKSHEET   **14**

Radioactive Particles

Use with Chapter 4,
Section 4.4

1. Which radioactive emission has the greatest mass? Least mass?
    Alpha particles have the greatest mass. Gamma rays have no mass.

2. Why do you think gamma rays are drawn as wavy lines?
    Answers may vary. Answers should include the fact that gamma rays have no mass and are often characterized as light (waves).

3. Which charged plate are the alpha particles attracted to? Explain.
    Because they have opposite charges, the positively charged alpha particles are attracted to the negatively charged plate.

4. Which charged plate are the beta particles attracted to? Why do the beta particles have a greater curvature than the alpha particles do?
    The beta particles are attracted to the positively charged plate. Their curvature is greater because they have a much smaller mass than alpha particles do and are therefore more greatly affected by the electric field.

5. Explain why the gamma rays do not bend toward one of the electrically charged plates.
    Gamma rays have no charge; therefore, they are not attracted to either charged plate.

TEACHING TRANSPARENCY WORKSHEET

15

The Electromagnetic Spectrum

**Use with Chapter 5,
Section 5.1**

1. What kinds of waves have the longest wavelength? What kinds of waves have the shortest wavelength?
   Radio waves are the longest waves. Gamma rays are the shortest waves.

2. Which waves have the lowest frequency?
   Radio waves have the lowest frequency.

3. Which has a higher frequency: microwaves or X rays?
   X rays (10^{18} s^{-1}) have a higher frequency than microwaves (10^{11} s^{-1}).

4. Which waves can be seen by the eye?
   The waves in the visible portion of the spectrum can be seen by the eye.

5. Sequence the different segments of the visible spectrum in order from shortest wavelength to longest wavelength.
   violet, blue, green, yellow, orange, red light

6. Sequence the following types of waves from lowest frequency to highest frequency: ultraviolet rays, infrared rays, gamma rays, radio waves, and green light.
   radio waves, infrared waves, green light, ultraviolet waves, gamma rays

7. Compare the wavelengths and frequencies of each kind of wave. What is the relationship between frequency and wavelength?
   Frequency and wavelength are inversely proportional. This means that as wavelength increases, frequency decreases and as frequency increases, wavelength decreases.

8. What is the wavelength of a radio station emitting its signal at 95.5 MHz? Estimate your answer to the nearest power of ten.
   The wavelength of a radio signal at 95.5 MHz is about 1 m long, or 10^0 m.

TEACHING TRANSPARENCY WORKSHEET

16

Atomic Orbitals

**Use with Chapter 5,
Section 5.2**

1. What is the shape of an s orbital?
   An s orbital is spherical.

2. What is the relationship between the size of an s orbital and the principal energy level in which it is found?
   The size of an s orbital increases with increasing principal energy level number.

3. What is the shape of a p orbital? How many p orbitals are there in a sublevel?
   A p orbital is dumbbell shaped. There are three p orbitals in a given sublevel.

4. How many electrons can each orbital hold?
   Each orbital can hold two electrons.

5. Look at the diagrams of the p orbitals. What do x, y, and z refer to?
   These letters refer to the three perpendicular axes; p orbitals are situated along these three axes in space.

6. How many d orbitals are there in a given sublevel? How many total electrons can the d orbitals in a sublevel hold?
   There are five d orbitals in a given sublevel. Therefore, the d orbitals in one sublevel can hold 10 electrons.

7. Which d orbitals have the same shape?
   d_{xy}, d_{xz}, d_{yz}, and $d_{x^2-y^2}$

8. What point in each diagram represents an atom's nucleus?
   The point where the x, y, and z axes intersect represents the location of an atom's nucleus.

9. How likely is it that an electron occupying a p or a d orbital would be found very near an atom's nucleus? What part of the diagram supports your conclusion?
   Very unlikely; the shapes of the orbitals come to a point at the intersection of the three axes, making the possibility of an electron being located there very unlikely.

Teaching Transparency Worksheets Answer Key   Chemistry: Matter and Change   **T169**

TEACHING TRANSPARENCY WORKSHEET

The Periodic Table

Use with Chapter 6, Section 6.1

18

1. How many elements are listed in the periodic table? **115**

2. What is the atomic number of selenium? **34**

3. What is the symbol for palladium? **Pd**

4. What is the atomic mass of strontium? **87.62 amu**

5. How are elements that are gases at room temperature designated in the periodic table? **Their boxes contain a red balloon.**

6. How many columns of elements does the periodic table contain? **18**

7. What is another name for a column of elements? **group or family**

8. What two group numbers can be used to designate elements in the second column of the periodic table? **group 2A or group 2**

9. How many rows of elements does the periodic table contain? **7**

10. What is another name for a row of elements? **period**

11. Which period contains the least number of elements? **period 1**

12. What element is found in period 4, group 7B? **manganese**

13. How are metals designated in the periodic table? **Their boxes are tinted blue.**

14. How are metalloids designated in the periodic table? **Their boxes are tinted green.**

15. How are nonmetals designated in the periodic table? **Their boxes are tinted yellow.**

16. What is the name of the group 1A elements (excluding hydrogen)? **alkali metals**

17. What is the name of the group 2A elements? **alkali earth metals**

18. What is the name of the group 7A elements? **halogens**

19. What is the name of the group 8A elements? **noble gases**

20. What can be said about the electron configurations of all the elements in a group? **Their valence electron configurations are identical.**

36 Chemistry: Matter and Change • Chapter 6

TEACHING TRANSPARENCY WORKSHEET

Orbital Filling Sequence and Energy Levels

Use with Chapter 5, Section 5.3

17

1. What does each small box in the diagram represent? **Each box represents an orbital.**

2. How many electrons can each orbital hold? **Each orbital can hold two electrons.**

3. How many electrons can the d sublevel hold? **A d sublevel can hold 10 electrons.**

4. Which is associated with more energy: a 2s or a 2p orbital? **A 2p orbital has more energy than a 2s orbital.**

5. Which is associated with more energy: a 2s or a 3s orbital? **A 3s orbital has more energy than a 2s orbital.**

6. According to the aufbau principle, which orbital should fill first, a 4s or a 3d orbital? **A 3d orbital has more energy than a 4s orbital, thus, the 4s orbital fills first.**

7. Which orbital has the least amount of energy? **The 1s orbital has the least amount of energy.**

8. What is the likelihood that an atom contains a 1s orbital? **All atoms have 1s orbitals.**

9. Sequence the following orbitals in the order that they should fill up according to the aufbau principle: 4d, 4p, 4f, 5s, 6s, 5p, 3d, 4s. **4s, 3d, 4p, 5s, 4d, 5p, 6s, 4f**

10. Write a general rule to describe the filling of orbitals in an atom. **Answers will vary. An orbital with lower energy is generally occupied by an electron before an orbital of higher energy is.**

34 Chemistry: Matter and Change • Chapter 5

TEACHING TRANSPARENCY WORKSHEET 19

The s-, p-, d-, and f-Block Elements

1. What are the four sections, or blocks, of the periodic table? **s-, p-, d-, and f-blocks**

2. What does each block represent? **Each block represents the energy sublevel being filled by valence electrons.**

3. What do elements in the s-block have in common? **They have valence electrons only in the s orbitals.**

4. What is the valence electron configuration of each element in group 1A? **s^1**

5. What is the valence electron configuration of each element in group 2A? **s^2**

6. Why does the s-block span two groups of elements? **The single s orbital can hold a maximum of two valence electrons.**

7. Why does the p-block span six groups of elements? **The three p orbitals can each hold a maximum of two electrons, thus, the p orbitals can contain a maximum of six valence electrons, which corresponds to the six columns spanned by the p-block.**

8. Why are there no p-block elements in period 1? **There are no p-block elements in period 1 because the p sublevel does not exist for the first principal energy level.**

9. What is the ending of the electron configuration of each element in group 4A? **p^2**

10. What is the electron configuration of neon? **$[He]2s^2 2p^6$**

11. In what period does the first d-energy sublevel appear? **period 4**

12. Why does the d-block span ten groups of elements? **The five d orbitals can each hold a maximum of two electrons, resulting in a total of ten possible valence electrons.**

13. What is the ending of the electron configuration of each element in group 3B? **d^1**

14. What is the electron configuration of titanium? **$[Ar]4s^2 3d^2$**

15. In what period does the first f-energy sublevel appear? **period 6**

16. Determine the group, period, and block for the element having the electron configuration $[Xe]4f^{14}5d^{10}6s^2 6p^3$.
a. group **5A**   b. period **6**   c. block **p**

TEACHING TRANSPARENCY WORKSHEET 20

Atomic and Ionic Radii

1. Which groups and periods of elements are shown in the table of atomic radii? **groups 1A–8A; periods 1–6**

2. In what unit is atomic radius measured? Express this unit in scientific notation. **picometer (pm); 10^{-12} m**

3. What are the values of the smallest and largest atomic radii shown? What elements have these atomic radii? **31 pm and 265 pm; helium and cesium, respectively**

4. What happens to atomic radii within a period as the atomic number increases? **The atomic radius of the elements within a period generally decreases as the atomic number of the elements increases.**

5. Cite any exceptions to the generalization you stated in your answer to question 4. **Exceptions are antimony (Sb) and tellurium (Te) in period 5, and bismuth (Bi) and polonium (Po) in period 6.**

6. What accounts for the trend in atomic radii within a period? **With increasing atomic number, the increased positive charge of the nucleus pulls more strongly on the outermost electrons, pulling them closer to the nucleus. Consequently, the atomic radius decreases.**

7. What happens to atomic radii within a group as the atomic number increases? **The atomic radius of the elements within a group generally increases as the atomic number of the elements increases.**

8. Cite any exceptions to the generalization you stated in your answer to question 7. **There are no exceptions.**

9. What accounts for the trend in atomic radii within a group? **With increasing atomic number, the increased pull by the larger positive charge of the nucleus is offset by the outer electrons' larger orbitals and by shielding by inner electrons. Consequently, the atomic radius increases.**

10. In the table of ionic radii, how is the charge of the ions of elements in groups 1A–4A related to the group number of the elements? **The charge of the ion of each element is the same as the element's group number.**

TEACHING TRANSPARENCY WORKSHEET

22

Use with Chapter 7,
Section 7.1

Elements in Food

1. Which elements listed in the chart are alkali metals? **sodium and potassium**

2. Which elements listed in the chart are alkaline earth metals? **calcium and magnesium**

3. Which elements in the chart are involved in the following body functions?

   a. activity of nervous system **calcium, sodium, potassium, and magnesium**

   b. bone formation **calcium and magnesium**

   c. activity of muscles **calcium, potassium, and magnesium**

4. The Food Guide Pyramid shows the numbers of servings of different food groups that people should eat every day to ensure they are getting the right amounts of nutrients. Use the Food Guide Pyramid to write a breakfast, lunch, and dinner menu for a single day that includes the recommended numbers of servings of the different food groups. Write your menu below. Identify the food group and the number of servings of each food. (Generally, one serving of a food is the amount of that food that fits in the palm of your hand.)

sample menus

Breakfast

Food	Element in Food	Food Group	Number of Servings
Oatmeal	Ca, Mg	Bread, cereal, rice, and pasta	2
Banana	K, Mg	Fruit	1
Toast (white)		Bread, cereal, rice, and pasta	1
Milk	Ca	Milk, yogurt, and cheese	1

Lunch

Food	Element in Food	Food Group	Number of Servings
Chicken (in sandwich)	Na	Meat, poultry, fish, dry beans, eggs, and nuts	1
Cheese (in sandwich)	Ca	Milk, yogurt, and cheese	1
Bread (wheat, in sandwich)	Ca, Mg	Bread, cereal, rice, and pasta	2
Salad	Na, K, Mg	Vegetable	2
Vinegar and oil dressing	Na	Fats, oils, and sweets	1
Yogurt	Ca	Milk, yogurt, and cheese	1

Dinner

Food	Element in Food	Food Group	Number of Servings
Fish	K	Meat, poultry, fish, dry beans, eggs, and nuts	2
Rice	Ca, Mg	Bread, cereal, rice, and pasta	2
Broccoli	Na, K, Mg	Vegetable	1
Salad	Na, K, Mg	Vegetable	1
Peaches and grapes	Mg	Fruit	2

TEACHING TRANSPARENCY WORKSHEET

21

Use with Chapter 6,
Section 6.3

First Ionization and Successive Ionization Energies

1. What is meant by first ionization energy?
   First ionization energy is the energy required to remove the first electron from a gaseous atom.

2. Which element has the smallest first ionization energy? The largest? What are their values?
   rubidium; helium; about 400 and 2375 kJ/mol, respectively

3. What generally happens to the first ionization energy of the elements within a period as the atomic number of the elements increases?
   The first ionization energy of the elements within a period generally increases as the atomic number of the elements increases.

4. What accounts for the general trend in the first ionization energy of the elements within a period?
   With increasing atomic number, the increased positive charge of the nucleus produces an increased hold on the valence electrons. Consequently, the first ionization energy increases.

5. What happens to the values of the successive ionization energies of an element?
   The values of the successive ionization energies increase.

6. Based on the graph, rank the group 2A elements in periods 1–5 in decreasing order of first ionization energy.
   beryllium, magnesium, calcium, strontium

7. How is a jump in ionization energy related to the valence electrons of the element?
   The jump occurs after the valence electrons have been removed.

8. What generally happens to the first ionization energy of the elements within a group as the atomic number of the elements increases?
   The first ionization energy of the elements within a group generally decreases as the atomic number of the elements increases.

9. What accounts for the general trend in the first ionization energy of the elements within a group?
   With increasing atomic number, the size of the atom increases and the valence electrons are father from the nucleus. Consequently, less energy is needed to remove them, and the first ionization energy decreases.

TEACHING TRANSPARENCY WORKSHEET

(24)

Transition Metals

Use with Chapter 7, Section 7.3

1. Of the metals listed on the map, how many are transition metals? List the transition metals.

   Of the 18 metals listed, 13 are transition metals: copper, nickel, zinc, platinum, tantalum, vanadium, tungsten, cobalt, chromium, cadmium, niobium, manganese, and gold.

2. The United States imports most of the chromium it uses to make products such as stainless steel. Name three countries with chromium deposits.

   Turkey, South Africa, and Botswana

3. The United States imports most of the manganese it needs. Manganese is a component of the hard steel used for heavy machinery. On which continents are there large deposits of manganese?

   South America, Africa, and Australia

4. The human body requires trace amounts of a number of transition metals. Which of these transition metals are listed on the map?

   Zinc, cobalt, manganese, chromium, and copper are required by the body in trace amounts and are listed on the map.

5. Which metal—vanadium, chromium, or manganese—has the highest melting point? Why?

   Chromium has the highest melting point because it has the most unpaired electrons—5 d electrons and 1 s electron.

6. What use do the metals found in the United Kingdom and New Caledonia have in common?

   Both platinum and nickel are used to control the conditions at which reactions can occur.

7. Explain why the nickel and copper ores mined in Canada are brightly colored. How can color be used to detect the charge on a transition metal ion?

   Nickel and copper have partially filled d sublevels. Electrons in these sublevels can absorb visible light of specific wavelengths. A change in the charge on an ion is often accompanied by a color change.

8. What property does the cobalt mined in Belgium have in common with the nickel mined in Norway?

   They are ferromagnetic elements that can form permanent magnets.

TEACHING TRANSPARENCY WORKSHEET

(23)

Properties of p-Block Elements

Use with Chapter 7, Section 7.2

1. What is the common name for group 7A? Which element in this group is the most reactive? Explain your answer.

   Halogen group; the most reactive halogen is fluorine because it has the greatest tendency to attract electrons (greatest electronegativity).

2. What are allotropes? Name three p-block elements that have allotropes.

   Allotropes are forms of an element that have different structures and properties when they are in the same state. Carbon, phosphorus, oxygen, and sulfur all have allotropes.

3. What roles do the period-2 elements in groups 4A–7A play in the chemistry of living organisms?

   Most substances that control what happens in cells contain carbon. Nitrogen is found in proteins. The oxygen produced during photosynthesis is used during cellular respiration. Fluorine protects tooth enamel from decay.

4. Explain why the noble gases are relatively unreactive.

   The noble gases are relatively unreactive because they have a filled outermost energy level.

5. Sulfur and fluorine combine to form the compound SF_6. What other elements might form a similar compound with fluorine? Explain why.

   Se and Te are in the same group as sulfur. Selenium (Se) and Tellurium (Te) combine with fluorine to form SeF_6 and TeF_6, respectively.

6. Oxides are compounds in which oxygen is combined with another element. Use the table to identify differences between the oxides of metals and nonmetals.

Oxide	Physical State at Room Temperature	Reaction
Aluminum oxide	Solid	Reacts with nitric acid to form aluminum nitrate
Sulfur dioxide	Gas	Reacts with water to give sulfuric and sulfurous acid
Carbon dioxide	Gas	Reacts with water to give carbonic acid
Magnesium oxide	Solid	Reacts with sulfuric acid to form magnesium sulfate

   Usually, oxides of metals are solids at room temperature, while those of nonmetals are gases. Metal oxides react with acids. Nonmetal oxides react with water to form an acid.

TEACHING TRANSPARENCY WORKSHEET

25

Formation of Ions

Use with Chapter 8,
Section 8.1

1. What are the names of the two elements shown?
calcium and oxygen

2. Are the elements shown on the left sides of the two equations neutral? How can you tell?
Yes; each contains equal numbers of protons and electrons.

3. What is the name for the energy needed to remove electrons from an atom, such as the Ca atom shown?
ionization energy

4. What kind of charge does the Ca atom take on as a result of the reaction? What is the name for an ion with that kind of charge?
positive; cation

5. What kind of charge does the O atom take on as a result of the reaction? What is the name for an ion with that kind of charge?
negative; anion

6. Is the outer electron configuration of the Ca atom before the reaction a very stable one? How can you tell?
No; it is not a stable octet of electrons.

7. Is the outer electron configuration of the O atom before the reaction a very stable one? How can you tell?
No; it is not a stable octet of electrons.

8. Is the outer electron configuration of the Ca ion after the reaction a very stable one? How can you tell?
Yes; it is a stable octet of electrons.

9. Is the outer electron configuration of the O ion after the reaction a very stable one? How can you tell?
Yes; it is a stable octet of electrons.

10. What is the electron configuration of the Ca ion? What neutral atom has the same configuration, and in what chemical family is it located in the periodic table?
$1s^2 2s^2 2p^6 3s^2 3p^6$, argon, a noble gas, has the same configuration.

11. What is the electron configuration of the O ion? What neutral atom has the same configuration, and in what chemical family is it located in the periodic table?
$1s^2 2s^2 2p^6$, neon, a noble gas, has the same configuration.

50   Chemistry: Matter and Change • Chapter 8   Teaching Transparency Worksheets

---

TEACHING TRANSPARENCY WORKSHEET

26

Ionic Bonds

Use with Chapter 8,
Section 8.2

1. How many valence electrons does a neutral magnesium (Mg) atom have?   **two**

2. What is the charge on a magnesium ion? What does magnesium have to do to form such an ion, and why does it tend to do so?
2+; it must lose its two valence electrons. It tends to do so to achieve the stable octet configuration of a noble gas.

3. How many valence electrons does a single neutral chlorine (Cl) atom have?   **seven**

4. What is the charge on a chloride ion? What does chlorine have to do to form such an ion, and why does it tend to do so?
1−; it must gain one electron. It tends to do so to achieve the stable octet configuration of a noble gas.

5. How many magnesium atoms and how many chlorine atoms react to form one formula unit of magnesium chloride? Why? What is the formula of magnesium chloride?
One Mg atom and two Cl atoms react because one 2+ ion and two 1− ions produce the required overall charge of zero. The formula is $MgCl_2$.

6. What kind of compound is magnesium chloride? What happens to electrons during the formation of the compound? What holds the atoms together in the compound?
Ionic; the two valence electrons of the magnesium atom are transferred, one to each of the chlorine atoms. The attraction of oppositely charged particles (the Mg^{2+} and the Cl^-) holds the atoms together, forming an ionic bond.

7. What is the formula of the ionic compound formed by magnesium and sulfur (S) atoms? Explain why, in terms of electron transfer, stability, and overall charge.
MgS; the Mg atom transfers its two valence electrons to the S atom. In that way, each achieves a stable noble-gas configuration. One Mg ion with a charge of 2+ is balanced by one S ion with a charge of 2−, producing a net overall charge of zero.

8. What is the formula of the ionic compound formed by magnesium and phosphorus (P) atoms? Explain why, in terms of electron transfer, stability, and overall charge.
Mg_3P_2; each Mg atom transfers its two valence electrons to the P atoms, each of which must gain three electrons. In that way, each achieves a stable noble-gas configuration. Three Mg ions, each with a charge of 2+, are balanced by two P ions, each with a charge of 3−, producing a net overall charge of zero.

52   Chemistry: Matter and Change • Chapter 8   Teaching Transparency Worksheets

---

28

Metallic Bonding

Use with Chapter 8,
Section 8.4

1. What is a regular, repeating three-dimensional arrangement of atoms called?
a crystal lattice

2. Do the separate electrons that are shown belong exclusively to a single atom? What word is used to describe such electrons?
no; delocalized

3. Are the electrons shown the only ones actually present? Why?
No; they are the valence electrons from the metal atoms.

4. Why are the central atoms shown as positively charged?
The delocalized negative electrons came from neutral atoms, thus leaving the atoms with a positive charge.

5. How does the number of separate electrons shown for the group 1A metal atoms compare to the number of atoms? Explain why in terms of valence electrons.
They are equal. Group 1A atoms have only one valence electron and thus only one electron that can become delocalized.

6. How does the number of separate electrons shown for the group 2A metal atoms compare to the number of atoms?
There are twice as many electrons as group 2A atoms.

7. What holds the metal atoms together in such an arrangement?
The delocalized electrons are simultaneously attracted to more than one metal cation.

8. What term is used to describe this model of metallic bonding? _____ **electron sea model**

9. How well do metals tend to conduct electricity? How does the model of metallic bonding account for that property?
Metals tend to conduct electricity well. The model's delocalized electrons are not held strongly by individual atoms and are thus able to move easily throughout the metal.

10. Do metals tend to be brittle, or are they malleable and ductile? How does the model of metallic bonding account for that property?
Metals are malleable and ductile. The model's delocalized electrons are able to move around the positive metal core atoms and keep the crystal from breaking during hammering or drawing into wire.

27

Formulas for Ionic Compounds

Use with Chapter 8,
Section 8.3

1. How many valence electrons are there in an atom of sodium (Na)? What would a sodium atom tend to do in bonding with another atom to form an ionic compound? Why?
One; it would tend to lose an electron because the loss would leave it with a stable octet of electrons, like that of a noble gas.

2. How many valence electrons are there in an atom of phosphorus (P)? What would a phosphorus atom tend to do in bonding with another atom to form an ionic compound? Why?
Five; it would tend to gain three electrons because the gain would give it a stable octet of electrons, like that of a noble gas.

3. What would be the formula and name of the ionic compound formed when sodium reacts with phosphorus? What are the oxidation numbers of each of the ions present?
Na_3P, **sodium phosphide;** Na^+, $+1$; P^{3-}, -3

4. How many valence electrons are in an atom of sulfur (S)? What would a sulfur atom tend to do in bonding with another atom to form an ionic compound? Why?
Six; it would tend to gain two electrons because the gain would give it a stable octet of electrons, like that of a noble gas.

5. What would be the formula and name of the ionic compound formed when sodium reacts with sulfur? What are the oxidation numbers of each of the ions present?
Na_2S, **sodium sulfide;** Na^+, $+1$; S^{2-}, -2

6. How many valence electrons are in an atom of aluminum (Al)? What would an aluminum atom tend to do in bonding with another atom to form an ionic compound? Why?
Three; it would tend to lose three electrons because the loss would leave it with a stable octet of electrons, like that of a noble gas.

7. What would be the formula and name of the ionic compound formed when sodium reacts with chlorine (Cl)? What would a chlorine atom tend to do in bonding with another atom to form an ionic compound? Why?
Seven; it would tend to gain one electron because the gain would give it a stable octet of electrons, like that of a noble gas.

8. What would be the formula and name of the ionic compound formed when aluminum reacts with chlorine? What are the oxidation numbers of each of the ions present?
$AlCl_3$, **aluminum chloride;** Al^{3+}, $+3$; Cl^-, -1

9. What would be the formula and name of the ionic compound formed when aluminum reacts with sulfur? What are the oxidation numbers of each of the ions present?
Al_2S_3, **aluminum sulfide;** Al^{3+}, $+3$; S^{2-}, -2

TEACHING TRANSPARENCY WORKSHEET (30)

VSEPR Model and Molecular Shape

1. The shapes of the molecules shown have been determined by means of the VSEPR model. What is the basic assumption of this model?
Pairs of electrons, either shared or unshared, repel each other as much as possible around a central atom.

2. How many lone pairs and how many shared pairs of electrons surround the boron (B) atom in the borane (BH_3) molecule shown?
no lone pairs; three shared pairs

3. What is the shape of the BH_3 molecule? Explain why.
The BH_3 molecule is trigonal planar. There are three electron pairs that repel so that they are as far as possible from one another. The shape that maximizes the distance is trigonal planar.

4. How many lone pairs and how many shared pairs of electrons surround the carbon (C) atom in the methane (CH_4) molecule shown? What is the shape of the molecule?
no lone pairs; four shared pairs; tetrahedral

5. How many lone pairs and how many shared pairs of electrons surround the nitrogen (N) atom in the ammonia (NH_3) molecule shown? What is the shape of the molecule?
one lone pair; three shared pairs; trigonal pyramidal

6. How many lone pairs and how many shared pairs of electrons surround the oxygen (O) atom in the water (H_2O) molecule shown? What is the shape of the molecule?
two lone pairs; two shared pairs; bent

7. How many lone pairs and how many shared pairs of electrons surround the fluorine (F) atom in the hydrogen fluoride (HF) molecule shown? What is the shape of the molecule?
three lone pairs; one shared pair; linear

TEACHING TRANSPARENCY WORKSHEET (29)

Lewis Structures

1. Step 1 in drawing the Lewis structure for a molecule is to decide which atoms of the molecule are most likely the terminal ones. In the transparency, why are the hydrogen (H) atoms in hydrazine (N_2H_4) shown as the terminal atoms?
A hydrogen atom can form only one bond, so it cannot be a central atom.

2. Step 2 in drawing a Lewis structure involves determining the total number of valence electrons in the atoms in the molecule. Explain why the total number of valence electrons in N_2H_4 is 14.
Each nitrogen (N) atom has five valence electrons and each hydrogen (H) atom has one valence electron, resulting in a total of $(2 \times 5) + (4 \times 1) = 14$.

3. Step 3 in drawing a Lewis structure requires finding the number of bonding pairs. What must be done to the result of step 2 to find the number of bonding pairs? Verify that this is so in the case of N_2H_4 in the transparency.
The total number of valence electrons from step 2 must be divided by 2; in the case of N_2H_4, $14/2 = 7$.

4. In step 4 in the transparency, one bonding pair has been placed between each pair of bonded atoms in N_2H_4. How many such bonding pairs are shown in step 4, and what symbol is used to represent them?
five; a line

5. Step 5 requires subtraction of the number of bonding pairs used in step 4 from the number of bonding pairs determined in step 3. Verify that the result is 2 for N_2H_4. Lone pairs are then placed around each terminal atom to achieve a full outer level, and any remaining pairs are assigned to the central atom(s). Explain the drawing that has resulted for N_2H_4.
$7 - 5 = 2$. Because the H atoms already had a complete outer level of electrons, a lone pair of electrons was positioned next to each N atom.

6. In step 6, if any central atom drawn in step 5 does not have an octet, lone pairs from the terminal atoms must be converted to double or triple bonds involving the central atom. Why was this extra step unnecessary in the case of N_2H_4?
The central N atoms already had complete octets, and the Lewis structure was already correct.

7. What number should be placed in the blank for step 2 for the silicon dioxide (SiO_2) molecule?
$4 + 6 + 6 = 16$, the total number of valence electrons

8. What number should be placed in the blank for step 3 for SiO_2?
$16/2 = 8$, the number of bonding pairs

TEACHING TRANSPARENCY WORKSHEET **32**

Parts of a Balanced Chemical Equation

Examine the parts of the chemical equation at the top of the transparency. Use this information to answer the following questions about Equation 1 and Equation 2.

1. Write Equation 1 as a sentence.
   Two units of potassium iodide in aqueous solution plus one unit of lead(II) nitrate in aqueous solution yield one unit of solid lead(II) iodide plus two units of potassium nitrate in aqueous solution.

2. Write Equation 2 as a sentence.
   Six units of hydrogen chloride in aqueous solution plus two atoms of solid aluminum yield two units of aluminum chloride in aqueous solution plus three molecules of hydrogen gas.

3. What substances are reactants in
   a. Equation 1? **KI, $Pb(NO_3)_2$**   b. Equation 2? **HCl, Al**

4. What substances are products in
   a. Equation 1? **PbI_2, KNO_3**   b. Equation 2? **$AlCl_3$, H_2**

5. List the coefficients used in
   a. Equation 1. **2, 1, 1, 2**   b. Equation 2. **6, 2, 2, 3**

6. What substances are in aqueous solution in
   a. Equation 1? **KI, $Pb(NO_3)_2$, KNO_3**   b. Equation 2? **HCl, $AlCl_3$**

7. What substance shown is a gas? **H_2**

8. What is the state of PbI_2 in Equation 1? **solid**

9. What state is not represented in either equation? **liquid**

10. What do the subscripts tell you in the formulas for
    a. $AlCl_3$? **Three atoms of chlorine exist in one unit of aluminum chloride.**
    b. KNO_3? **Three atoms of oxygen exist in one unit of potassium nitrate.**
    c. $Pb(NO_3)_2$? **Each nitrate ion contains three oxygen atoms, and two nitrate ions exist in each unit of lead (II) nitrate.**

TEACHING TRANSPARENCY WORKSHEET **31**

Electronegativity and Polarity

1. What is electronegativity?
   Electronegativity is the tendency of an atom to attract electrons.

2. The electronegativities of the elements of period 2 and of group 17 of the periodic table are shown. What trends in electronegativity do you see across the period? Down the group?
   Electronegativity increases from left to right across the period and decreases down the group.

3. When there is an electronegativity difference between two covalently bonded atoms, what is true of the bond between them? Toward which of the atoms are the shared electrons more attracted?
   The covalent bond is polar; toward the more electronegative atom.

4. What kind of bond exists between a carbon (C) atom and a chlorine (Cl) atom? (Assume that a bond is nonpolar covalent if the electronegativity difference is 0, polar covalent if the difference is greater than 0 but not more than 1.70, and ionic if the difference is more than 1.70.)
   3.16 − 2.55 = 0.61, polar covalent bond

5. Given your answer to question 4 and your knowledge of molecular shapes, is a carbon tetrachloride (CCl_4) molecule polar or nonpolar? Explain.
   CCl_4 is a nonpolar molecule because its symmetrical tetrahedral shape results in a balancing of the partial charges resulting from each polar covalent bond.

6. What kind of bond exists between a nitrogen (N) atom and a fluorine (F) atom? Is a nitrogen trifluoride (NF_3) molecule polar or nonpolar? Explain.
   3.98 − 3.04 = 0.94, polar covalent bond; NF_3 is a polar molecule because its asymmetrical, trigonal pyramidal shape does not balance its partial charges.

7. What kind of bond exists between a beryllium (Be) atom and a bromine (Br) atom? Is a beryllium bromide ($BeBr_2$) molecule polar or nonpolar? Explain.
   2.96 − 1.57 = 1.39, polar covalent bond; $BeBr_2$ is a nonpolar molecule because its symmetrical, linear shape balances its partial charges.

8. What kind of bond exists between a beryllium (Be) atom and a fluorine (F) atom?
   3.98 − 1.57 = 2.41, ionic bond

9. What kind of bond exists between a boron (B) atom and an iodine (I) atom? Is a boron triiodide (BI_3) molecule polar or nonpolar? Explain.
   2.66 − 2.04 = 0.62, polar covalent bond; BI_3 is a nonpolar molecule because its symmetrical, trigonal planar shape balances its partial charges.

TEACHING TRANSPARENCY WORKSHEET

34

The Activity Series

Use with Chapter 10,
Section 10.2

1. For each of the following pairs of elements, underline the one that would replace the other element in a compound.

   a. <u>calcium</u>, tin

   b. <u>bromine</u>, fluorine

   c. aluminum, <u>potassium</u>

   d. <u>zinc</u>, sodium

   e. iron, <u>copper</u>

   f. iodine, <u>chlorine</u>

   g. silver, <u>lead</u>

2. For each of the following reactants, use the activity series to determine whether the reaction would take place or not. If no reaction takes place, write NR in the blank. If a reaction does take place, write the formulas for the products of the reaction. (Hint: If an active metal replaces the hydrogen in water, the hydroxide of the active metal forms.)

   a. $Li(s) + Fe(NO_3)_3(aq) \rightarrow$ ___$LiNO_3(aq) + Fe(s)$___

   b. $Au(s) + HCl(aq) \rightarrow$ ___NR___

   c. $Cl_2(g) + KBr(aq) \rightarrow$ ___$KCl(aq) + Br_2(l)$___

   d. $Cu(s) + Al(NO_3)_3(aq) \rightarrow$ ___NR___

   e. $Ag(s) + HBr(aq) \rightarrow$ ___NR___

   f. $Ni(s) + SnCl_2(aq) \rightarrow$ ___$Sn(s) + NiCl_2(aq)$___

3. Magnesium metal can be used to remove tarnish from silver items. Silver tarnish is the corrosion that occurs when silver metal reacts with substances in the environment, especially those containing sulfur. Why would magnesium remove tarnish from silver? **Magnesium is more active than silver and will replace it in silver compounds, restoring the silver metal.**

4. Use the activity series for metals to explain why copper metal is used in plumbing where the water might contain compounds of many different metals. **Copper is not an active metal. It would not replace the metals in the compounds in the water.**

5. The last four metals in the activity series of metals are commonly referred to as the "coinage metals." Why would these metals be chosen over more active metals for use in coins? Why do you think some more active metals, such as zinc or nickel, are sometimes used in coins? **Copper, silver, platinum, and gold would be more durable because they will not react as readily with substances in the environment. The more active metals are somewhat durable and cost less.**

TEACHING TRANSPARENCY WORKSHEET

33

Balancing Chemical Equations

Use with Chapter 10,
Section 10.1

1. Examine the following equation.

   $$Mg(s) + Ag_2S(s) \rightarrow MgS(s) + Ag(s)$$

   a. How many atoms of magnesium are on each side of the equation? **1**

   b. Which element does not have the same number of atoms on both sides of the equation? **silver**

   c. Write the balanced equation for this reaction. ___$Mg(s) + Ag_2S(s) \rightarrow MgS(s) + 2Ag(s)$___

2. Follow the steps for balancing a chemical equation and write a response for each step for the reaction in which iron metal (Fe) burns in oxygen (O_2) to form iron(III) oxide (Fe_2O_3).

   Step 1: **$Fe(s) + O_2(g) \rightarrow Fe_2O_3(s)$**

   Step 2: **1 atom of Fe, 2 atoms of O**

   Step 3: **2 atoms of Fe, 3 atoms of O**

   Step 4: **$4Fe(s) + 3O_2(g) \rightarrow 2Fe_2O_3(s)$**

   Step 5: **They are in the lowest ratio.**

   Step 6: **There are 4 Fe atoms and 6 O atoms on both sides of the equation.**

3. For each of the following, use at least one of the rules for balancing equations to explain why the equation is not properly balanced. Then write a correctly balanced equation for each reaction.

   a. $2H_2O(l) + 2CO_2(g) \rightarrow 2H_2CO_3(aq)$
   The coefficients are not in the lowest possible ratio;
   $H_2O(l) + CO_2(g) \rightarrow H_2CO_3(aq)$

   b. $MgNO_{32}(aq) + 2K(s) \rightarrow Mg(s) + 2KNO_3(aq)$
   Because parentheses were not used around the nitrate ion, the nitrogen and oxygen atoms are not balanced; $Mg(NO_3)_2(aq) + 2K(s) \rightarrow Mg(s) + 2KNO_3(aq)$

   c. $AlCl_3(aq) + AgNO_3(aq) \rightarrow AgCl(s) + Al(NO_3)_3(aq)$
   The number of chlorine, nitrogen, and oxygen atoms are not the same on both sides; $AlCl_3(aq) + 3AgNO_3(aq) \rightarrow 3AgCl(s) + Al(NO_3)_3(aq)$

TEACHING TRANSPARENCY WORKSHEET

35

Summary of Reaction Types

Use with Chapter 10,
Section 10.2

1. For each set of reactants listed below, identify the type of reaction that the reactants might undergo. List as many reaction types as may apply. Assume that all the reactants for the reaction are listed.

   a. a compound and an element   **synthesis, combustion, single-replacement**

   b. two compounds   **double-replacement, synthesis**

   c. one compound   **decomposition**

2. For each set of reaction products listed below, identify the type of reaction that might have formed the products. List as many reaction types as may apply. Assume that all the products for the reaction are listed.

   a. a compound and an element   **single-replacement, decomposition**

   b. two compounds   **double-replacement, combustion, decomposition**

   c. one compound   **synthesis, combustion**

3. Classify each of the following examples according to the type of reaction involved. List as many reaction types as may apply.

   a. A match burns.
   combustion

   b. The carbonic acid found in soft drinks breaks down into bubbles of carbon dioxide and water.
   decomposition

   c. Phosphorous and oxygen react rapidly, forming diphosphorous pentoxide.
   combustion, synthesis

   d. An iron nail is placed into a copper sulfate solution. Copper metal appears on the nail.
   single-replacement

   e. The acid in baking powder reacts with baking soda ($NaHCO_3$), forming carbon dioxide gas and other products.
   double-replacement

   f. Water and sulfur trioxide react to form sulfuric acid.
   synthesis

   g. Copper wire is placed in a silver nitrate solution. The solution turns blue, which is the color of the copper ion, and solid silver forms on the wire.
   single-replacement

TEACHING TRANSPARENCY WORKSHEET

36

Types of Equations

Use with Chapter 10,
Section 10.3

1. Write the complete equation as a sentence.
   Two units of potassium hydroxide in aqueous solution react with one unit of sulfuric acid to yield one unit of potassium sulfate in aqueous solution and liquid water.

2. What is a spectator ion?
   an ion that is present but does not participate in the reaction

3. What are the spectator ions in this reaction?
   K^+, SO_4^{2-}

4. Compare and contrast each pair below.

   a. complete equations, complete ionic equations
   Both show all reactants and products, but a complete ionic equation shows ionic compounds as ions, not as formula units.

   b. complete ionic equations, net ionic equations
   A complete ionic equation shows all species in solution; a net ionic equation does not include spectator ions and shows only those species that actually undergo chemical change.

5. For the reaction between aqueous silver nitrate and aqueous sodium chloride, write each of the following. The products of the reaction are aqueous sodium nitrate and solid silver chloride.

   a. complete equation
   $AgNO_3(aq) + NaCl(aq) \rightarrow NaNO_3(aq) + AgCl(s)$

   b. complete ionic equation
   $Ag^+(aq) + NO_3^-(aq) + Na^+(aq) + Cl^-(aq) \rightarrow Na^+(aq) + NO_3^-(aq) + AgCl(s)$

   c. net ionic equation
   $Ag^+(aq) + Cl^-(aq) \rightarrow AgCl(s)$

6. What is the net ionic equation for the reaction between aqueous calcium hydroxide and nitric acid? The products of this reaction are aqueous calcium nitrate and water. How does this net ionic equation compare to the net ionic equation shown on the transparency?
   $OH^-(aq) + H^+(aq) \rightarrow H_2O(l)$; they are the same.

TEACHING TRANSPARENCY WORKSHEET 38

Mass-to-Mass Conversions

Use with Chapter 12, Section 12.2

1. What conversion factor would you use to convert correctly from the mass of a given substance to the number of moles of the given substance?
   1 mol of given substance/molar mass of given substance

2. What conversion factor would you use to convert correctly from the number of moles of a given substance to the number of moles of an unknown substance?
   moles of unknown substance/moles of given substance

3. What conversion factor would you use to convert correctly from the number of moles of the unknown substance to the mass of the unknown substance?
   molar mass of unknown substance/1 mol of unknown substance

4. What is the name of the conversion factor in question 2?
   the mole ratio

5. What do you need to know to find the conversion factor in question 2?
   the balanced chemical equation for the reaction

Use the following balanced chemical equation and table to answer questions 6.

$$2N_2(g) + O_2(g) \rightarrow 2N_2O(g)$$

Compound	Molar Mass (g/mol)
N_2	28.02
O_2	32.00
N_2O	44.02

6. Write the conversion factors in the order you would use them to determine correctly each of the following.

   a. the number of moles of N_2O produced when 26.5 g N_2 reacts with excess oxygen
   1 mol N_2/28.02 g N_2, 2 mol N_2O/2 mol N_2

   b. the mass of N_2 needed to produce 11.5 g N_2O
   1 mol N_2O/44.02 g N_2, 2 mol N_2/2 mol N_2O, 28.02 g N_2/1 mol N_2

   c. the mass of N_2 needed to react completely with 1.56 g O_2
   1 mol O_2/32.00 g O_2, 2 mol N_2/1 mol O_2, 28.02 g N_2/1 mol N_2

   d. the mass of N_2O produced when 7.05 g O_2 reacts with excess nitrogen
   1 mol O_2/32.00 g O_2, 2 mol N_2O/1 mol O_2, 44.02 g N_2O/1 mol N_2O

TEACHING TRANSPARENCY WORKSHEET 37

Mass-to-Mole and Mole-to-Particles Conversions for Compounds

Use with Chapter 11, Section 11.3

1. According to the diagram, what *three* quantities can you calculate if you know the number of moles of a compound?
   the mass of the compound, the number of moles of atoms or ions in the compound, and the number of representative particles of the compound

2. According to the diagram, what *three* quantities can you calculate from a mass measurement of a compound?
   the number of moles of the compound, the number of moles of atoms or ions in the compound, and the number of representative particles of the compound

3. If you were given the number of moles of a compound, what quantity would you need to know to calculate the mass of that number of moles of the compound?
   the molar mass of the compound

4. If you were given the number of moles of a compound, what information would you need to know to determine each of the conversion factors necessary to find the number of moles of each atom or ion in the compound?
   the chemical formula of the compound

5. You are given a 2.0-mol sample of calcium carbonate ($CaCO_3$). The molar mass of $CaCO_3$ is 100.09 g/mol. Write the conversion factor you would use to determine correctly each of the following quantities.

   a. the mass in grams of the sample
   100.09 g $CaCO_3$/1 mol $CaCO_3$

   b. the number of formula units of $CaCO_3$ in the sample
   6.02 × 10^{23} formula units $CaCO_3$/1 mol $CaCO_3$

   c. the number of moles of oxygen atoms in the sample
   3 mol atoms O/1 mol $CaCO_3$

6. Write the conversion factors in the order you would use them to determine correctly each of the following quantities in a sample of 2.0 × 10^{-4} molecules of ethane (C_2H_6). The molar mass of ethane is 30.08 g/mol.

   a. the mass in grams of the sample
   1 mol C_2H_6/6.02 × 10^{23} molecules C_2H_6, 30.08 g C_2H_6/1 mol C_2H_6

   b. the number of carbon atoms in the sample
   1 mol C_2H_6/6.02 × 10^{23} molecules C_2H_6, 2 mol atoms C/1 mol C_2H_6

Name _____ Date _____ Class _____

TEACHING TRANSPARENCY WORKSHEET 39

Limiting Reactants

Use with Chapter 12, Section 12.3

1. How many N_2 molecules are shown in the transparency? N atoms?
   3 molecules N_2; 6 atoms N

2. How many H_2 molecules are shown? H atoms?
   3 molecules H_2; 6 atoms H

3. What is the ratio of H atoms to N atoms in one NH_3 molecule?
   3 atoms H : 1 atom N

4. How many H atoms would be needed to react with all the N atoms shown in the transparency?
   6 atoms N × 3 atoms H/1 atom N = 18 atoms H

5. How many N atoms would be needed to react with all the H atoms shown in the transparency?
   6 atoms H × 1 atom N/3 atoms H = 2 atoms N

6. According to your answers to questions 4 and 5, how many N_2 molecules and H_2 molecules will be used up completely by the reaction shown in the transparency?
   1 molecule N_2 and 3 molecules H_2

7. Which reactant will remain after the reaction? How many molecules?
   N_2; 2 molecules N_2

8. Complete the diagram below by drawing the products of the chemical reaction in the box.

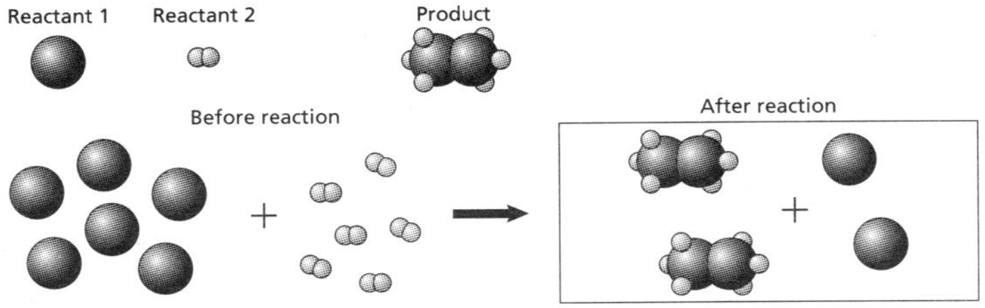

Reactant 1   Reactant 2   Product

Before reaction

After reaction

9. Which reactant in the diagram is the limiting reactant?
   reactant 2

10. Which reactant in the diagram is in excess?
    reactant 1

Name _____ Date _____ Class _____

TEACHING TRANSPARENCY WORKSHEET 40

Manometer

Use with Chapter 13, Section 13.1

1. The transparency shows a manometer. Briefly describe its parts.
   The manometer consists of a U-shaped glass tube closed at one end and attached to a flask that contains no gas. The tube is partially filled with mercury. There is a vacuum above the mercury in the tube.

2. Why are the levels of the mercury in the two arms of the U-tube the same when there is no gas in the flask?
   There is no gas in the flask or the closed end of the tube. Thus, no pressure is being exerted on the surface of the mercury in either arm of the U-tube.

3. What happens when gas enters the flask?
   The gas in the flask exerts pressure on the surface of the mercury in the arm of the U-tube attached to the flask and pushes down on it. The downward push on the mercury in this arm causes the mercury to rise in the closed-end arm.

4. Compare the force exerted by the gas to the force exerted by the mercury contained in the portion of the closed-end arm labeled Δh.
   The forces are equal.

5. If the flask was filled with air at a pressure of 1.00 atm, what would be the value of Δh in millimeters of Hg?
   760 mm Hg

6. If the flask was filled with air at a pressure of 0.50 atm, what would be the value of Δh in millimeters of Hg?
   760 mm Hg/1.00 atm × 0.50 atm = 380 mm Hg

7. A sample of gas is collected in the flask. The value of Δh is 76.0 mm Hg. What is the pressure of the gas in mm Hg? In atm?
   76.0 mm Hg
   76.0 mm Hg × 1.00 atm/760 mm Hg = 0.100 atm

8. How does the vapor pressure of mercury affect the pressure reading of the manometer?
   The pressure reading of the manometer is the sum of the partial pressures of mercury and the gas.

TEACHING TRANSPARENCY WORKSHEET 42

Pressure vs. Volume Graph

Use with Chapter 14,
Section 14.1

1. Based on this graph, how is the volume of a gas affected by increased pressure at constant temperature?

   At constant temperature, the volume of a gas decreases with increased pressure.

2. The relationship between the volume and pressure of a gas at constant temperature is an inversely proportional relationship. Based on the evidence in this graph, define the inversely proportional relationship.

   As one variable (either volume or pressure) increases, the other variable decreases.

3. What do you notice when you multiply the pressure by the volume for any point on the line on the graph?

   At constant temperature, the volume of a gas when multiplied by its pressure always equals the same number. For example, at one liter of volume, the pressure of this gas is 200 kPa. One liter multiplied by 200 kPa equals 200 L·kPa. Similarly, 2L·100 kPa and 4L·50 kPa both equal 200 L·kPa.

4. Based on the mathematical relationship derived from this graph, what is the pressure of the gas at 3.00 L at constant temperature?

   The pressure is P·3.00 L = 200 L·kPa; P = 66.7 kPa.

5. What gas law does this graph represent?

   This graph represents Boyle's law.

6. What mathematical expression is used to define this law? Define all symbols used.

   $P_1V_1 = P_2V_2$, where P_1 represents the initial pressure of the gas, P_2 represents the final pressure of the gas, V_1 represents the initial volume of the gas, and V_2 represents the final volume of the gas.

7. A sample of gas is compressed from 3.25 L to 1.20 L at constant temperature. If the pressure of this gas in the 3.25-L volume is 100.00 kPa, what will the pressure be at 1.20 L? List all known and unknown variables. Show all your work.

   Known variables: $V_1 = 3.25$ L; $V_2 = 1.20$ L; $P_1 = 100.00$ kPa

   Unknown variable: $P_2 = ?$ kPa

   Solve for the unknown: $P_1V_1 = P_2V_2$; $P_2 = P_1(V_1/V_2)$;

   $P_2 = 100.00$ kPa (3.25 L/1.20 L); $P_2 = 271$ kPa

TEACHING TRANSPARENCY WORKSHEET 41

Phase Diagrams

Use with Chapter 13,
Section 13.4

1. What variables are plotted on a phase diagram?

   pressure and temperature

2. How many phases of water are represented in its phase diagram? What are they?

   three; solid, liquid, and vapor

3. Use the phase diagram for water to complete the following table.

Temperature (°C)	Pressure (atm)	Phase
200	1	vapor
−2	1	solid
150	100	liquid
−2	0.001	vapor
30	0.8	liquid
0.00 < T < 100.00	1	liquid
100.00	< 1.00 atm	vapor

4. What phases of water coexist at each point along the red curve?

   solid and liquid

5. What two phase changes occur at each point along the yellow curve in the phase diagram for water?

   sublimation and deposition

6. Look at the phase diagram for carbon dioxide. Above which pressure and temperature is carbon dioxide unable to exist as a liquid?

   73 atm, 31°C

7. At which pressure and temperature do the solid, liquid, and gaseous phases of carbon dioxide coexist?

   5.1 atm, −57°C

TEACHING TRANSPARENCY WORKSHEET

44

Burning of Methane Gas

Use with Chapter 14, Section 14.4

1. What do the coefficients in chemical equations involving gases, solids, and liquids represent?

   The coefficients in chemical equations represent all relative numbers of particles.

2. What does Avogadro's principle state?

   Avogadro's principle states that each mole of any gas occupies 22.4 L at STP.

3. Based on Avogadro's principle, the coefficients in chemical equations involving only gases represent two types of quantities. Name the two quantities.

   The coefficients in chemical equations involving only gases represent all relative numbers of particles and relative volumes.

4. Based on the balanced equation for the complete combustion of methane, how many liters of carbon dioxide, $CO_2(g)$, and water vapor, $H_2O(g)$, are produced by the complete combustion of 1 L of methane gas, CH_4?

   When 1 L of methane gas reacts with oxygen, 1 L of carbon dioxide and 2 L of water vapor are produced.

5. What volume of oxygen gas is needed for the complete combustion of 8.00 L of methane gas, CH_4? Assume that the pressure and temperature of the reactants are the same. Show all your work.

   Known: $V_{CH_4} = 8.00$ L   Unknown: $V_{O_2} = ?$ L

   Using the balanced equation given, 2 L O_2/1 L CH_4

   Multiply the known volume of CH_4 by the volume ratio to find the volume of O_2.

   $V_{O_2} = (8.00 \text{ L } CH_4) (2 \text{ L } O_2/1 \text{ L } CH_4) = 16.0 \text{ L } O_2$

6. Write a balanced equation for the complete combustion of propane gas, C_3H_8, with oxygen, O_2, to form carbon dioxide, CO_2, and water, H_2O.

   $C_3H_8(g) + 5O_2(g) \rightarrow 3CO_2(g) + 4H_2O(g)$

7. What volume of carbon dioxide gas, CO_2, is produced when 7.00 L of propane gas, C_3H_8, undergoes complete combustion, as shown in your answer to question 6? Show all your work.

   Known: $V_{C_3H_8} = 7.00$ L   Unknown: $V_{CO_2} = ?$ L

   Using the balanced equation from question 6, 3 L CO_2/1 L C_3H_8

   Multiply the known volume of C_3H_8 by the volume ratio to find the volume of CO_2.

   $V_{CO_2} = (7.00 \text{ L } C_3H_8)(3 \text{ L } CO_2/1 \text{ L } C_3H_8) = 21.0 \text{ L } O_2$

TEACHING TRANSPARENCY WORKSHEET

43

Volume vs. Temperature Graph

Use with Chapter 14, Section 14.1

1. Notice that this graph shows kelvin temperatures. How are the kelvin scale and Celsius scale related mathematically?

   $T_K = 273 + T_C$ where T_K is a temperature measurement using the kelvin scale, and T_C is a temperature measurement using the Celsius scale.

2. Based on this graph, how is the volume of a gas affected by increased temperature at constant pressure?

   At constant pressure, the volume of a gas increases with increased temperature.

3. The relationship between the volume and temperature of a gas at constant pressure is a directly proportional relationship. Based on the evidence in this graph, define the directly proportional relationship.

   As one variable (either volume or temperature) increases, the other variable increases.

4. What do you notice when you divide the temperature by the volume for any point on the line on the graph?

   At constant pressure, the kelvin temperature of a gas when divided by its volume always equals the same number. For example, at 200 K, the volume of this gas is 1 L. 200 K divided by 1 L equals 200 K/L. Similarly, 600 K/3 L and 1000 K/5 L both equal 200 K/L.

5. What law does this graph represent?

   This graph represents Charles's law.

6. What mathematical expression is used to define this law? Define all symbols used.

   $V_1/T_1 = V_2/T_2$, where V_1 represents the initial volume of the gas, T_1 represents the initial kelvin temperature of the gas, V_2 represents the final volume of the gas, and T_2 represents the final kelvin temperature of the gas.

7. The kelvin temperature of a sample of gas is decreased from 460 K to 240 K at constant pressure. If the volume of this gas at 460 K is 2.50 L, what will the volume be at 240 K? List all known and unknown variables. Show all your work.

   Known variables: $T_1 = 460$ K; $T_2 = 240$ K; $V_1 = 2.50$ L

   Unknown variable: $V_2 = ?$ L

   Solve for the unknown: $V_1/T_1 = V_2/T_2$; $V_2 = V_1 (T_2/T_1)$:

   $V_2 = 2.50$ L (240 K/460 K); $V_2 = 1.3$ L

Teaching Transparency Worksheets Answer Key   Chemistry: Matter and Change   **T183**

Name _____ Date _____ Class _____

Solubility–Temperature Graphs

1. What variables are plotted on the graph? **solubility and temperature**

2. What is the unit of each variable?
solubility: g solute/100 g H₂O; temperature: °C

3. Use the graph to complete the table below.

Substance	Solubility at 10°C
Calcium chloride (CaCl₂)	64 g CaCl₂/100 g H₂O
Cerium(III) sulfate (Ce₂(SO₄)₃)	10 g Ce₂(SO₄)₃/100 g H₂O
Potassium chloride (KCl)	30 g KCl /100 g H₂O
Potassium chlorate (KClO₃)	5 g KClO₃/100 g H₂O
Sodium chloride (NaCl)	36 g NaCl /100 g H₂O

4. At what temperature are sodium chloride and potassium chloride equally soluble
in water? **30°C**

5. How does the solubility of cerium(III) sulfate differ from the solubility of potassium
chlorate over the temperature range 0°C–100°C?
The solubility of cerium(III) sulfate decreases over the temperature range
0°C–100°C, whereas the solubility of potassium chlorate increases over the same
temperature range.

6. How many grams of sodium chloride will dissolve in 1.0 kg of water at 20°C?
(1.0 kg H₂O)(1000 g/1 kg)(36 g NaCl/100 g H₂O) = 360 g NaCl

7. Explain whether increasing temperature has a greater effect on the solubility of KCl or
on the solubility of NaCl.
The line of the solubility graph of KCl shows a sharper rise than the line of the
solubility graph of NaCl as temperature is increased. The sharper rise indicates
that the solubility of KCl increases more than the solubility of NaCl.

8. Explain how you might make a solution containing 42 g KCl dissolved in 100 g H₂O at a
temperature of 40°C. What term describes this type of solution?
Heat 100 g of water to a temperature of 50°C. Add 42 g KCl and stir until
dissolved. Slowly cool the solution, without disturbing it, to 40°C. The resulting
KCl solution is a supersaturated solution.

Name _____ Date _____ Class _____

Phase Diagram of Solvent and Solution

1. What variables are plotted on the phase diagram? **pressure and temperature**

2. What solvent is represented in the phase diagram? **water**

3. What phases of the solvent are represented in the diagram? **gas, liquid, and solid**

4. What do the solid lines represent?
The solid lines represent the pressures and temperatures at which two phases of
the pure solvent (water) coexist.

5. What is the term applied to a solution in which water is the solvent? **aqueous solution**

6. What do the dashed lines represent?
The dashed lines represent the pressures and temperatures at which two phases
of the aqueous solution coexist.

7. At each temperature, what does ΔP represent?
ΔP represents the lowering of the vapor pressure due to the addition of
the solute.

8. At any temperature, how does the vapor pressure of the aqueous solution compare with
the vapor pressure of the pure solvent?
The vapor pressure of the aqueous solution is always lower than the vapor
pressure of the pure solvent.

9. Will a solution boil at the same temperature as the pure solvent under normal atmospheric pressure? Explain.
No; a liquid boils when its vapor pressure equals atmospheric pressure. Because
the vapor pressure of a solution is always less than the vapor pressure of the pure
solvent at the same temperature, the solution can never boil under normal
atmospheric pressure at the same temperature as the pure solvent.

10. What must you do to the temperature of a solution to make it boil if it is at the boiling
point of the pure solvent under normal atmospheric pressure?
raise its temperature

11. How does the freezing point of a solution compare with the freezing point of the pure
solvent at the same pressure?
The freezing point of the solution is lower.

TEACHING TRANSPARENCY WORKSHEET

48

Temperature Changes of Water

Use with Chapter 16,
Section 16.3

1. The graph shows what happens when ice, at −40°C, is gradually heated to more than 120°C. What is happening in the region between −40°C and 0°C?
20 kcal of heat is being added to the ice. The ice remains a solid even though its temperature rises 40 degrees.

2. At 0°C, the temperature does not change even though 80 kcal of heat is added. Why does the temperature not change?
During this period, the ice is melting, and liquid and solid water coexist. All the heat that is absorbed is converting the solid to the liquid, so the temperature does not change as long as both states coexist.

3. What is happening in the region between 0°C and 100°C?
Because all the solid water has been converted to liquid water, the 100 kcal of heat that is being added increases the temperature of the water.

4. When the water reaches 100°C, the temperature does not change even though 540 kcal of heat is added. Why does the temperature not change?
When the temperature reaches 100°C, the liquid water boils, and liquid and gaseous water coexist. All the heat that is being absorbed is converting the liquid to the gas, so the temperature does not change as long as both states coexist.

5. Compare the amount of heat needed to convert liquid water to water vapor with the amount needed to convert ice to liquid water. Explain the difference.
More heat is needed to convert liquid water to water vapor than is needed to convert ice to liquid water. That is because it takes more energy to separate the particles in liquid far enough to form a gas than it takes for water molecules in a solid to slide past each other to form a liquid.

6. What is happening in the region above 100°C?
All the water is in the gaseous state, and the temperature of the gas rises as more heat is added.

7. If you continue to add heat, what will happen to the water vapor?
Its temperature will continue to increase.

TEACHING TRANSPARENCY WORKSHEET

47

Using a Calorimeter

Use with Chapter 16,
Section 16.2

1. The calorimeter shown on the transparency is used to measure the caloric content of foods. To do this, a sample of food is burned inside the reaction chamber of the calorimeter. What is the system? What are the surroundings?
The system is the reaction inside the chamber. The surroundings are everything except the system.

2. What besides food must be added to the chamber? Explain why.
Oxygen gas must be added because combustion requires oxygen.

3. What are the products of the reaction that takes place in the reaction chamber?
The products are principally carbon dioxide gas, water vapor, and heat.

4. Why is the calorimeter insulated?
The insulation prevents heat from escaping.

5. What does the thermometer measure?
The thermometer measures the temperature of the water surrounding the reaction chamber.

6. Describe the movement of heat as the reaction takes place inside the chamber.
The heat released from the combustion reaction moves from the chamber to the water surrounding the chamber.

7. Assuming that no heat escapes from the calorimeter, what equation would you use to determine the amount of heat released by the burning food in the reaction chamber? Define all variables in the equation.
$q = c \times m \times \Delta T$, **where q is the amount of heat absorbed by the water, c is the specific heat of water, m is the mass of the water in the calorimeter, and ΔT is the change in the temperature of the water.**

8. Does the answer obtained from the equation in question 7 have a positive or negative value? Explain why. What is the sign of ΔH for the reaction?
The answer has a positive value because ΔT is positive. Combustion is an exothermic reaction.

Teaching Transparency Worksheets Answer Key   Chemistry: Matter and Change   **T185**

TEACHING TRANSPARENCY WORKSHEET

Changes in Enthalpy and Entropy

49

Use with Chapter 16,
Sections 16.4 and 16.5

1. What do the arrows on the transparency represent?
The arrows represent the enthalpy changes in the formation of liquid water from the elemental forms of hydrogen and oxygen, in the vaporization of liquid water, and in the decomposition of gaseous water to elemental hydrogen and oxygen.

2. Why do the arrows vary in direction?
Arrows that point upward indicate that energy is absorbed, or the process is endothermic. The downward arrow indicates that energy is released, or the process is exothermic.

3. What can you conclude about the transitions and the magnitudes of the enthalpies shown on the transparency?
The enthalpy of transition from liquid water to the elemental forms of hydrogen and oxygen (286 kJ) is equal to the sum of the enthalpy for transition from liquid water to gaseous water (44 kJ) and the enthalpy for transition of gaseous water to the elemental forms of hydrogen and oxygen (242 kJ).

4. How does Hess's law apply to your answer to question 3?
Hess's law states that the enthalpy for an overall reaction (the transition from liquid water to the elemental forms of hydrogen and oxygen) is the sum of the enthalpies for the individual component reactions (the transition from liquid water to gaseous water plus the transition of gaseous water to the elemental forms of hydrogen and oxygen).

5. What do the ball models for liquid water and gaseous water on the transparency show?
The molecules of liquid water are closer together than the molecules of gaseous water.

6. What do the ball models indicate about the overall order of the molecules?
As the molecules move farther apart, they become more disordered.

7. When molecules become more ordered or disordered, what happens to the entropy?
Increased disorder means that entropy has increased. Decreased disorder means that entropy has decreased.

TEACHING TRANSPARENCY WORKSHEET

Factors That Affect Reaction Rate

50

Use with Chapter 17,
Section 17.2

1. Look at the sequence of pictures. What happened to the apple over time?
The color of the apple changed from white to dark brown.

2. No chemical was added to the apple. Explain why the apple changed.
A chemical in the apple reacted with the air, producing a brown substance.

3. How could you test your answer to question 3?
Answers will vary. A possible answer is to put a sliced apple in a vacuum. If the apple does not darken, the test indicates that air is needed for the reaction to occur.

4. What effect would increasing the amount of air surrounding the apple have on the apple? Explain your answer.
Increasing the amount of air would cause the apple to change color faster because more air particles would be colliding with the chemical particles in the apple and therefore the reaction would occur faster.

5. How would slicing the apple into more pieces affect the apple? Explain your answer.
Slicing the apple into more pieces would increase the apple's surface area. Therefore, more air molecules would react with the chemicals in the apple, and more of the apple would turn brown.

6. The apple in the pictures is raw. A cooked apple would not change the same way. Give a possible reason why.
Answers may vary. The cooking process involves heat, which changes the chemical makeup of the apple. Because the chemicals in the apple have changed, their reaction with air will also change.

Name _____ Date _____ Class _____

Reaction Rate

1. What does the graph show?
   The graph shows a decrease in hydrogen peroxide concentration over time.

2. Is the hydrogen peroxide a reactant or product in the reaction? How do you know?
   The hydrogen peroxide is a reactant because its concentration decreases over time.

3. The hydrogen peroxide is part of a decomposition reaction. Write a balanced equation for the reaction.
   $2H_2O_2(aq) \rightarrow 2H_2O(l) + O_2(g)$

4. From the graph, what can you conclude about the rate of this reaction?
   The rate of the reaction decreases over time.

5. Define the term *instantaneous rate*.
   Instantaneous rate is the rate of a reaction at a specific time.

6. How can you use the graph to find the instantaneous rate of the reaction that you identified in your answer to question 3? Give your answer in mathematical terms.
   The instantaneous rate can be found by finding the slope of the straight line that is tangent to the curve at a specific point. The slope is defined mathematically as
   $\Delta[H_2O_2]/\Delta t$.

7. To show the complete relationship of reactants to products in this reaction, what else would you need to plot on the graph?
   The concentrations of the products, water and oxygen, as a function of time also are needed.

8. What would you expect your answer to question 7 to show?
   The concentrations of the products should show an increase over time.

Name _____ Date _____ Class _____

Reaction Order

1. What is formed when the two solutions mix?
   A yellow precipitate, lead iodide, is formed.

2. Explain how the substance is formed in terms of the particles in the two solutions.
   The particles in the two solutions collide when the solutions mix. Some of these particles stick together and fall out of solution.

3. On the basis of the image in the transparency, what can you conclude about the rate of the reaction? Explain your answer.
   The reaction rate is very fast. The precipitate forms as soon as the two solutions mix.

4. On the basis of your answer to question 3, what can you conclude about the activation energy for the reaction?
   The activation energy must be low.

5. What can you conclude about the reaction order for the reaction?
   Reaction orders are determined by experimental measurements. Because the information provided does not contain any experimental information, no conclusions can be made about the reaction order.

6. If the rate equation is determined to be $k[Pb^{2+}][I^-]$, what is the reaction order?
   The reaction order will be first order in Pb^{2+}, first order in I^-, and second order overall.

7. Would you classify the reaction as exothermic, endothermic, nonspontaneous, or spontaneous. Explain your answer.
   The reaction is spontaneous because it produces a precipitate immediately when the two starting solutions mix. The formation of a precipitate means that energy is lost from the system, so the reaction is exothermic.

Teaching Transparency Worksheets Answer Key   Chemistry: Matter and Change   **T187**

Worksheet 53

Name _____ Date _____ Class _____

Chemical Equilibrium

Use with Chapter 18,
Section 18.1

53

1. Write the equilibrium constant expressions for the reactions on the transparency.

A $K_{eq} = [NO]^4[H_2O]^6/[NH_3]^4[O_2]^5$

B $K_{eq} = [N_2O_4]/[NO_2]^2$

C $K_{eq} = [NH_3]^2/[N_2][H_2]^3$

D $K_{eq} = [Ag(NH_3)_2{}^+]/[Ag^+][NH_3]^2$

E $K_{eq} = [N_2][H_2O]^2/[NO]^2[H_2]^2$

F $K_{eq} = [CO][Cl_2]/[COCl_2]$

G $K_{eq} = [H_3O^+][CN^-]/[HCN]$

H $K_{eq} = [H_2][CO_2]/[H_2O][CO]$

2. What is heterogeneous equilibrium?
A heterogeneous equilibrium is one in which the reactants and products are in more than one physical state.

3. Which equilibrium reactions are homogeneous equilibriums?
Equations a, b, c, d, e, f, and h are homogeneous equilibriums.

4. Which equilibrium reaction is a heterogeneous equilibrium?
Equation g is a heterogeneous equilibrium.

5. When writing equilibrium constant expressions, pure solids and liquids are not included. Why? Why do you include all reactants of equation D in its equilibrium constant expression?
Pure solids and liquids have an unchanging concentration that is incorporated into the value of the ratio. In equation d, the products and reactants are in an aqueous solution and are not considered to be pure substances.

6. If the K_{eq} for one of the reactions was 35.6, what would you know about the equilibrium?
At equilibrium, there are substantially more products present than reactants.

Worksheet 54

Name _____ Date _____ Class _____

How Changing Concentration Affects Equilibrium

Use with Chapter 18,
Section 18.2

54

1. Why do the changes shown in equations 1 and 2 cause the equilibrium to move to the right? What other changes in concentration would also cause a shift to the right?
The equilibrium in 1 moves to the right to relieve the stress caused by the increased concentration of CO(g). Adding H_2(g) would also shift the equilibrium to the right. The equilibrium in 2 moves to the right to relieve the stress caused by the decreased concentration of H_2O(g). Removing CH_4(g) would also shift the equilibrium to the right.

2. Why do the changes shown in equations 3 and 4 cause the equilibrium to move to the left? What other changes in concentration would also cause a shift to the left?
The equilibrium in 3 moves to the left to relieve the stress caused by the decreased concentration of CO(g). Removing H_2(g) would also shift the equilibrium to the left. The equilibrium in 4 moves to the left to relieve the stress caused by the increased concentration of H_2O(g). Adding CH_4(g) would also shift the equilibrium to the left.

3. What effect would decreasing the volume of the reaction container have on the equilibrium? Why?
Decreasing the volume of the reaction container would push the equilibrium to the right. A smaller number of moles will be more easily contained in a smaller volume. There are fewer moles of gas on the right and so the equilibrium shifts in that direction.

4. When does changing the volume of the reaction container not affect the equilibrium?
Changing the volume of the reaction container does not affect the equilibrium when an equal number of moles are on each side of the equation.

5. The production of methane and water vapor from carbon monoxide and hydrogen gas is an exothermic reaction. What does this tell you about how an increase in temperature would affect the equilibrium of this reaction? How would it affect the equilibrium constant?
Raising the temperature would favor the reaction to the left. A shift to the left relieves the stress placed on the system by consuming heat. This makes the equilibrium constant smaller because the reactants would be favored over the products.

6. When does changing the temperature not affect a reaction at equilibrium?
Changing the temperature always affects equilibrium.

TEACHING TRANSPARENCY WORKSHEET 55

Name _____ Date _____ Class _____

Use with Chapter 19, Section 19.1

Ionization of a Triprotic Acid

1. H_3AsO_4 is a triprotic acid. What does the term *triprotic* mean?
   containing three ionizable hydrogen atoms

2. What do all three of these equations have in common?
   Water accepts a hydrogen ion from the acid, forming a hydronium ion and
   an anion.

3. What property of water causes the ionization of H_3AsO_4 in aqueous solution?
   Water molecules are polar. The negative ends of water molecules attract
   hydrogen ions that are in the acid.

4. Which step would require the least energy? Explain.
   The first step would require the least energy because a proton is removed from
   an uncharged particle. In the other steps, a proton is removed from a negatively
   charged particle, which requires more energy.

5. Why are double arrows used in the questions shown?
   Although the hydrogen ion in the first equation is the most easily lost, none of
   the reactions go to completion but reach equilibrium, which is represented by
   double arrows.

6. Write a similar set of equations for the complete ionization of phosphoric acid (H_3PO_4), which is another triprotic acid.
   $H_3PO_4(aq) + H_2O(l) \rightleftharpoons H_3O^+(aq) + H_2PO_4^-(aq)$; $H_2PO_4^-(aq) + H_2O(l) \rightleftharpoons H_3O^+(aq) +$
   $HPO_4^{2-}(aq)$; $HPO_4^{2-}(aq) + H_2O(l) \rightleftharpoons H_3O^+(aq) + PO_4^{3-}(aq)$

7. The formula for citric acid is $H_3C_6H_5O_7$. How many steps would occur in the complete ionization of citric acid? Explain.
   Three; although there are more than three hydrogen atoms present in a citric
   acid molecule, only the three hydrogen atoms listed first in the formula are
   ionizable.

TEACHING TRANSPARENCY WORKSHEET 56

Name _____ Date _____ Class _____

Use with Chapter 19, Section 19.2

Ionization Equations and Constants

1. Why do some acids have more than one ionization equation?
   An acid has as many ionization equations as it has ionizable hydrogen atoms.

2. How do you know that the acids listed in the table are listed from strongest to weakest?
   The smaller the K_a, the weaker is the acid. The K_a for the ionization of the first
   H^+ ion decreases for each acid in the table going from top to bottom.

3. Which is stronger, the conjugate base of carbonic acid or the conjugate base of phosphoric acid? Explain.
   The conjugate base of carbonic acid is stronger. The weaker the acid is, the
   stronger is its conjugate base. Carbonic acid is weaker than phosphoric acid.

4. Write all the ionization equations for phosphorous acid (H_3PO_3), a weak acid.
   $H_3PO_3 \rightleftharpoons H^+ + H_2PO_3^-$
   $H_2PO_3^- \rightleftharpoons H^+ + HPO_3^{2-}$
   $HPO_3^{2-} \rightleftharpoons H^+ + PO_3^{3-}$

5. Write the ionization constant expression for these acids.
   a. hypochlorous acid $K_a = [H^+][ClO^-]/[HClO]$
   b. methanoic acid $K_a = [H^+][HCOO^-]/[HCOOH]$

6. Why can you assume that the concentrations of the ions in the ionization constant expression for a weak acid are equal?
   One anion forms for each hydrogen ion formed.

TEACHING TRANSPARENCY WORKSHEET

58

Use with Chapter 19, Section 19.4

Titration Graphs

1. NaOH is a strong base, HCl is a strong acid, and HCOOH is a weak acid.

   a. Which titration is between a strong acid and a strong base?

   Titration A

   b. Which titration is between a weak acid and a strong base?

   Titration B

2. What generalization can be made about the pH of the solution resulting from a complete reaction between a strong acid and a strong base?

   The solution is neutral, with a pH of 7.

3. Does the graph for Titration A support your answer to question 2? Explain.

   Yes; the equivalence point for the reaction, which shows when the reaction is complete, indicates a pH of 7.

4. What generalization can be made about the pH of the solution resulting from a complete reaction between a strong base and a weak acid?

   The solution is slightly basic, with a pH slightly greater than 7.

5. Does the graph for Titration B support your answer to question 4? Explain.

   Yes; the equivalence point for the reaction, which shows when the reaction is complete, indicates a pH slightly greater than 7.

6. During Titration A, what was the pH after 40.0 mL of NaOH was added to the HCl?

   2

7. What was the pH after 40.0 mL of NaOH was added to the HCOOH during Titration B?

   slightly less than 6

8. From the curves of the titrations, explain how you would know the equivalence point was near if a pH meter was used instead of an indicator.

   The change in pH would become more rapid with each drop of NaOH added.

9. Why was phenolphthalein a better choice for an indicator in Titration B than it would have been for Titration A?

   The end point for phenolphthalein occurs when the solution is slightly basic, which is appropriate for the equivalence point in Titration B. The equivalence point in Titration A occurs before the end point for phenolphthalein is reached.

TEACHING TRANSPARENCY WORKSHEET

57

Use with Chapter 19, Section 19.3

The pH Scale

1. What is the pH of a solution with a $[H^+]$ of 10^{-8}? **8**

2. What is the pOH of a solution with a $[OH^-]$ of 10^{-11}? **11**

3. What is the pH of a solution that has a $[OH^-]$ of 10^{-2}? **12**

4. What is the pOH of a solution that has a $[H^+]$ of 10^{-5}? **9**

5. What do you notice about the product of $[H^+]$ and $[OH^-]$ for any aqueous solution?

   It equals 10^{-14}.

6. What do you notice about the sum of pH and pOH for any aqueous solution?

   It equals 14.

7. Which is more acidic, a solution with a pH of 6 or one with a pH of 9?

   a solution with a pH of 6

8. Which is more basic, a solution with a pOH of 7 or one with a pOH of 12?

   a solution with a pOH of 7

9. Which is more acidic, a solution with a pH of 5 or one with a pOH of 10?

   a solution with a pOH of 10

10. Which is more basic, a solution with a pH of 8 or one with a pOH of 12?

    a solution with a pH of 8

11. Stomach contents can have a pH of 3. Are stomach contents acidic, basic, or neutral?

    acidic

12. Pure water has a pOH of 7. Is pure water acidic, basic, or neutral?

    neutral

13. Normal rain has a pH of approximately 6. Is normal rain strongly acidic, slightly acidic, neutral, slightly basic, or strongly basic?

    slightly acidic

14. Acid precipitation is often a problem in industrialized areas. What might you expect the pH of acid rain to be?

    less than that of normal rain, or less than 6

TEACHING TRANSPARENCY WORKSHEET

60

Equations for Redox Reactions

1. Did the bromide ion accept or donate an electron in this reaction? How do you know?
Donate; its oxidation number increased.

2. Locate the ion that has no change in oxidation number in this reaction.

    a. What is the term applied to an ion that is present but does not enter into the actual
chemical reaction? **spectator ion**

    b. What ion in this equation is this type of ion? **K^+**

3. Write the balanced net ionic equation for this reaction. What ion in the complete chemical equation is not included in the net ionic equation?
$2Br^-(aq) + Cl_2(aq) \longrightarrow 2Cl^-(aq) + Br_2(aq); K^+$

4. What generalization can you make about what happens to an oxidizing agent during a
redox reaction? Explain.
An oxidizing agent is reduced in a redox reaction because it gains electrons.

5. What generalization can you make about what happens to a reducing agent during a
redox reaction? Explain.
A reducing agent is oxidized in a redox reaction because it loses electrons.

6. Compare what happens in the equation on the transparency to what happens in the
following equation:
$$Fe(s) + 2HCl(aq) \longrightarrow FeCl_2(aq) + H_2(g)$$

    a. Assign an oxidation number to each ion, atom, or molecule shown in the above equation.
reactants: Fe, 0; H, +1; Cl, −1; products: Fe, +2; Cl, −1; H, 0

    b. What is oxidized? **Fe**

    c. What is reduced? **H^+**

    d. What is the oxidizing agent? **H^+**

    e. What is the reducing agent? **Fe**

    f. What has no change in oxidation number? **Cl^-**

TEACHING TRANSPARENCY WORKSHEET

59

Oxidation and Reduction

1. How do you know that the reaction for the chemical equation shown on the transparency
is a redox reaction?
Electron transfer from one atom to another takes place.

2. What element is oxidized? **magnesium, Mg**

3. How do you know the element is oxidized?
The magnesium atoms lost electrons.

4. What ion is formed as the result of this oxidation? **Mg^{2+}**

5. What element is reduced? **oxygen, O_2**

6. How do you know the element is reduced?
The oxygen atoms gained electrons.

7. What ion is formed as the result of this reduction? **O^{2-}**

8. How many electrons were transferred during this reaction as it is shown? Explain.
Four; each of two magnesium atoms transferred two electrons to each oxygen atom.

9. Assuming the atoms shown are the only ones available, could magnesium atoms be
oxidized if oxygen atoms were not reduced? Explain.
No; the sodium atoms could not lose electrons if no atoms accepted them.

10. Draw a diagram similar to the one on the transparency to show what happens during the
redox reaction between one atom of magnesium and a fluorine molecule.

11. In the reaction from question 10, what element is oxidized? **magnesium, Mg**

12. What ion is formed from this oxidation? **Mg^{2+}**

13. What element is reduced? **fluorine, F**

14. What ion is formed from this reduction? **fluoride, F^-**

15. How many electrons were transferred during this reaction as it is shown? Explain.
Two; the magnesium atom transferred an electron to each of two fluorine atoms.

TEACHING TRANSPARENCY WORKSHEET

62

Half-Reactions

1. In terms of electron transfer, what has happened in all of the oxidation half-reactions listed in the table?

   Iron atoms each lose three electrons.

2. In terms of electron transfer, what has happened in all of the reduction half-reactions listed in the table?

   The atom or ion being reduced gains electrons.

3. In all of these reactions, iron metal is oxidized. Is iron metal ever reduced? Explain.

   Fe^0 forms only positive ions. Going from an oxidation number of 0 to a positive oxidation number is always oxidation. Iron metal is never reduced.

4. Can iron ions be oxidized? Can they be reduced? Explain.

   Because Fe^{3+} can change to Fe^{2+} and Fe^0 by gaining electrons but cannot change to a higher oxidation state, it can be reduced but not oxidized. Fe^{2+} can be oxidized to Fe^{3+} or reduced to Fe^0.

5. In which of the reactions shown in the table are spectator ions present? For each reaction that contains a spectator ion, identify the spectator ion.

   D: Br^-; E: NO_3^-; F: SO_4^{2-}

6. Use the half-reaction method to balance equations B–F from the table.

   B. $Fe + Cl_2 \rightarrow FeCl_3$

   $2Fe + 3Cl_2 \rightarrow 2FeCl_3$

   C. $Fe + F_2 \rightarrow FeF_3$

   $2Fe + 3F_2 \rightarrow 2FeF_3$

   D. $Fe + HBr \rightarrow FeBr_3 + H_2$

   $2Fe + 6HBr \rightarrow 2FeBr_3 + 3H_2$

   E. $Fe + AgNO_3 \rightarrow Fe(NO_3)_3 + Ag$

   $Fe + 3AgNO_3 \rightarrow Fe(NO_3)_3 + 3Ag$

   F. $Fe + CuSO_4 \rightarrow Cu + Fe_2(SO_4)_3$

   $2Fe + 3CuSO_4 \rightarrow 3Cu + Fe_2(SO_4)_3$

TEACHING TRANSPARENCY WORKSHEET

61

Balancing Equations: Oxidation-Number Method

1. Use the rules shown on the transparency to balance the equation for the reaction that occurs when you place solid magnesium into nitric acid (HNO_3). Aqueous magnesium nitrate and hydrogen gas form.

   a. Step 1: $Mg + HNO_3 \rightarrow Mg(NO_3)_2 + H_2$

   b. Step 2: $\underset{0}{Mg} + \underset{+1\ -1}{H}\underset{+2}{N}\underset{-1}{O_3} \underset{0}{} \rightarrow Mg(NO_3)_2 + H_2$

   $Mg + HNO_3 \rightarrow Mg(NO_3)_2 + H_2$

   c. Step 3: $\overset{+2}{\overbrace{}}$
   $Mg + HNO_3 \rightarrow Mg(NO_3)_2 + H_2$
   $\underset{-1}{\underbrace{}}$

   d. Step 4: $Mg + 2HNO_3 \rightarrow Mg(NO_3)_2 + H_2$

   e. Step 5: **They are balanced.**

2. Use the rules shown on the transparency to balance the equation for the reaction that occurs when you mix solutions of nitric acid (HNO_3), potassium chromate (K_2CrO_4), and iron(II) nitrate ($Fe(NO_3)_2$). Aqueous potassium nitrate, iron(III) nitrate, and chromium(III) nitrate form, along with water.

   a. Step 1: $HNO_3 + K_2CrO_4 + Fe(NO_3)_2 \rightarrow KNO_3 + Fe(NO_3)_3 + Cr(NO_3)_3 + H_2O$

   b. Step 2: $\underset{+1\ -1}{HNO_3} + \underset{+1\ +6\ -2}{K_2CrO_4} + \underset{+2\ -1}{Fe(NO_3)_2} \rightarrow \underset{+1\ -1}{KNO_3} + \underset{+3\ -1}{Fe(NO_3)_3} + \underset{+3\ -1}{Cr(NO_3)_3} + \underset{+1\ -2}{H_2O}$

   c. Step 3: $\underset{+1}{\underbrace{\overset{-3}{\overbrace{}}}}$
   $HNO_3 + K_2CrO_4 + Fe(NO_3)_2 \rightarrow KNO_3 + Fe(NO_3)_3 + Cr(NO_3)_3 + H_2O$

   d. Step 4: $HNO_3 + K_2CrO_4 + 3Fe(NO_3)_2 \rightarrow KNO_3 + 3Fe(NO_3)_3 + Cr(NO_3)_3 + H_2O$

   e. Step 5: $8HNO_3 + K_2CrO_4 + 3Fe(NO_3)_2 \rightarrow 2KNO_3 + 3Fe(NO_3)_3 + Cr(NO_3)_3 + 4H_2O$

TEACHING TRANSPARENCY WORKSHEET

64

Use with Chapter 21,
Section 21.2

Hydrogen–Oxygen Fuel Cell

1. What half-cell reaction takes place in the anode?
$H_2 \rightarrow 2H^+ + 2e^-$

2. What half-cell reaction takes place in the cathode?
$\frac{1}{2}O_2 + 2H^+ + 2e^- \rightarrow H_2O$

3. What type of reaction (oxidation or reduction) takes place in the anode and in the cathode?
anode ___**oxidation**___ cathode ___**reduction**___

4. Write the overall cell reaction.
$2H_2(g) + O_2(g) \rightarrow 2H_2O(l)$

5. Represent the cell symbolically, using vertical lines to separate the components.
$H_2 \mid H^+ \parallel O_2 \mid H_2O$

6. Use the following standard reduction potentials to calculate the standard cell potential, E^0_{cell}.

$2H^+ + 2e^- \rightarrow H_2 \qquad \frac{1}{2}O_2 + 2H^+ + 2e^- \rightarrow H_2O$
$E^0 = 0.0000 \qquad\qquad E^0 = +1.229 \text{ V}$

$E^0_{cell} = E^0_{reduction} - E^0_{oxidation} = +1.229 \text{ V} - 0.0000 \text{ V} = +1.229 \text{ V}$

7. What is the main useful product of the hydrogen–oxygen fuel cell?
electricity

8. Compare and contrast this cell reaction with the burning of hydrogen in air.
Both processes are redox reactions with the same chemical reactants and products. In a fuel cell, however, the half-reactions are separated, electrons flow through an external circuit, the reaction is very controlled, and most of the chemical energy is converted to electrical energy instead of heat.

TEACHING TRANSPARENCY WORKSHEET

63

Use with Chapter 21,
Section 21.1

Electrochemical Cell

1. What half-cell reaction takes place in each beaker?
Left beaker ___ $Zn(s) \rightarrow Zn^{2+}(aq) + 2e^-$
Right beaker ___ $Cu^{2+}(aq) + 2e^- \rightarrow Cu(s)$

2. What type of reaction (oxidation or reduction) takes place in each beaker?
Left beaker ___**oxidation**___ Right beaker ___**reduction**___

3. Which electrode is the anode and which is the cathode?
Anode ___**left (zinc)**___ Cathode ___**right (copper)**___

4. What atomic particles move through the wire, and in which direction do they move?
electrons, from the left (zinc) electrode to the right (copper) electrode

5. Which ions flow from the salt bridge into each beaker?
Left beaker ___**Cl⁻ ions**___ Right beaker ___**K⁺ ions**___

6. Write the overall cell reaction.
$Zn(s) + Cu^{2+}(aq) \rightarrow Zn^{2+}(aq) + Cu(s)$

7. Represent the cell symbolically, using vertical lines to separate the components.
$Zn \mid Zn^{2+} \parallel Cu^{2+} \mid Cu$

8. Use the following standard reduction potentials to calculate the standard cell potential, E^0_{cell}.

$Zn^{2+} + 2e^- \rightarrow Zn \qquad Cu^{2+} + 2e^- \rightarrow Cu$
$E^0_{Zn} = -0.7618 \text{ V} \qquad E^0_{Cu} = +0.3419 \text{ V}$

$E^0_{cell} = E^0_{reduction} - E^0_{oxidation} = +0.3419 \text{ V} - (-0.7618 \text{ V}) = +1.1037 \text{ V}$

9. How is an electrochemical cell useful?
The electric current it produces in the wire can be used to power electric devices, such as lights and motors.

TEACHING TRANSPARENCY WORKSHEET

Electrolysis of Brine

65

Use with Chapter 21,
Section 21.3

1. What two half-cell reactions are possible at the anode?
$2Cl^-(aq) \rightarrow Cl_2(g) + 2e^-$

$2H_2O(l) \rightarrow O_2(g) + 4H^+(aq) + 4e^-$

2. Which of these two reactions is more likely to occur at the anode if a high concentration of chloride ions is present? Why?
The chloride reaction; chloride ions give up electrons more readily than do

water molecules.

3. What two half-cell reactions are possible at the cathode?
$Na^+(aq) + e^- \rightarrow Na(s)$

$2H_2O(l) + 2e^- \rightarrow H_2(g) + 2OH^-(aq)$

4. Which of these two reactions is more likely to occur at the cathode? Why?
The water reaction; water accepts electrons more readily than do sodium ions.

5. Write the overall cell reaction.
$2H_2O(l) + 2NaCl(aq) \rightarrow H_2(g) + Cl_2(g) + 2NaOH(aq)$

6. Identify the products labeled A, B, and C on the transparency. (Hint: A and B are gases.)
A ___ Cl_2 ___ B ___ H_2 ___ C ___ NaOH ___

7. Why is the hydrolysis of brine useful?
All three products—hydrogen gas, chlorine gas, and sodium hydroxide—are

commercially important to industry.

8. What must be done to cause the hydrolysis of brine to occur?
An electric current must be passed between the anode and the cathode from an

outside source.

9. In what geographic areas do you think it would be most economical to set up this process? Why?
It would be most economical near an ocean or salt lake, since brine (salt water)

would be readily available there.

TEACHING TRANSPARENCY WORKSHEET

Isomers

66

Use with Chapter 22,
Section 22.4

1. Which pair(s) of isomers represent structural isomers?
B, C, and E

2. Which pair(s) of isomers represent stereoisomers?
A and D

3. Which pair(s) of isomers represent geometric isomers?
A

4. Which pair(s) of isomers represent optical isomers?
D

5. Which pair(s) of isomers would you expect to have different melting points, boiling points, and densities?
A, B, C, and E

6. Which pair(s) of isomers would you expect to have different chemical properties? (Include properties related to chemical reactions where chirality is important.)
A, B, C, D, and E

7. Which pair(s) of isomers would rotate the plane of polarized light in opposite directions?
D

8. Name the isomers in pair E.
2,2-dimethylbutane (on the left) and hexane (on the right)

9. Which isomer in pair A is in the *cis-* form, the one on the left or the one on the right?
the isomer on the right

10. Which pair(s) of isomers have an asymmetric carbon?
D

Name _____ Date _____ Class _____

TEACHING TRANSPARENCY WORKSHEET **67**

Structure of Benzene

Use with Chapter 22, Section 22.4

1. How many carbon atoms and hydrogen atoms does a molecule of benzene have?
   six carbon atoms and six hydrogen atoms

2. Is benzene a saturated hydrocarbon?
   no

3. What does the double-donut shape on the transparency represent?
   It represents three pairs of electrons that are delocalized, or shared among all six carbon atoms in the ring.

4. The drawing below shows what Kekulé proposed for the structure of benzene. How is this structure similar to the structure shown on the transparency?

   Answers may vary. Both structures have six carbon atoms and six hydrogen atoms. Both are ring structures.

5. How does the structure proposed by Kekulé differ from the structure shown on the transparency?
   In the structure proposed by Kekulé, the two electrons that form the second bond of each double bond are localized between two specific carbon atoms. In the structure shown on the transparency, these electrons are delocalized.

6. If the structure proposed by Kekulé actually existed, would you expect it to be more reactive or less reactive than benzene? Why?
   The structure proposed by Kekulé should be more reactive than benzene. Electrons shared by just two carbon nuclei are easier to pull away than electrons shared by six carbon nuclei.

7. In the space below, draw another way to represent the structure of benzene that agrees with what chemists know about the properties of benzene.

Name _____ Date _____ Class _____

TEACHING TRANSPARENCY WORKSHEET **68**

Naming Halocarbons

Use with Chapter 23, Section 23.1

1. What is the name for any non-carbon or non-hydrogen group, such as a halogen, that is present in an organic molecule and reacts in a certain way?
   a functional group

2. What is the name for any halocarbon in which the halogen is covalently bonded to an aliphatic carbon atom?
   an alkyl halide

3. What is the name of the compound labeled A? Would the movement of the chlorine atom to another position on the two-carbon chain create a different compound?
   chloroethane; no

4. What is the name of compound B? Why are numbers necessary in naming it?
   1,1-dichloroethane; more than one dichloroethane compound can exist, depending on the positions of the chlorine atoms, so numbers are needed to distinguish them.

5. What is the name of compound C? Compare the name of compound C to that of compound B, and explain your answer.
   1,1-dichloroethane; the names are the same because the two compounds are the same. The compounds are simply shown reversed relative to each other.

6. What is the name of compound D? **1,2-dichloroethane**

7. What rule is followed in naming halocarbons that have two different types of halogens? How are the numbers assigned?
   The halogens are listed alphabetically. Numbers are assigned so as to give the lowest position number to the halogen that comes first in the alphabet.

8. What is the name of compound E? **bromochloromethane**

9. What is the name of compound F? **1-bromo-2-chloroethane**

10. What is the name of compound G? **2-bromo-2-chloro-3-fluoropentane**

11. What is the name for any halocarbon in which the halogen is covalently bonded to a benzene ring or other aromatic group?
    an aryl halide

12. What is the name of compound H? **1,2-diiodobenzene**

13. What is the name of compound I?
    1,3-dibromo-4-chlorobenzene

TEACHING TRANSPARENCY WORKSHEET

Alcohols, Ethers, and Amines

Use with Chapter 23, Section 23.2

69

1. What are the name and formula of the functional group in alcohols? **hydroxyl group, –OH**

2. With what suffix do the names of alcohols end? **-ol**

3. How is the position of the functional group indicated in naming alcohols? **by means of a number followed by a dash placed at the beginning of the name**

4. What structure is characteristic of ether molecules? **an oxygen atom bonded to two carbon atoms**

5. In naming ethers, what rule is applied if an ether's alkyl groups are different? **The alkyl groups are listed in alphabetical order, followed by the word ether.**

6. What structure is characteristic of amine molecules? **a nitrogen atom bonded to a carbon atom**

7. Name the compounds labeled A–E.
   compound A **ethylmethyl ether**
   compound B **1-propylamine**
   compound C **1-propanol**
   compound D **1,3-propyldiamine**
   compound E **1,3-propanediol**

8. Of compounds A, B, and C, which is likely to be a weak base? **compound B**

9. Of compounds A, B, and C, which is likely to have the lowest boiling point? **compound A**

10. Of compounds A, B, and C, which is most likely to have an offensive odor? **compound B**

TEACHING TRANSPARENCY WORKSHEET

Carbonyl, Carboxyl, and Amide Groups

Use with Chapter 23, Section 23.3

70

1. What is the name of the functional structural group that all the compounds shown have in common? Describe that structure. **the carbonyl group, which is made up of an oxygen atom and a carbon atom double-bonded to each other**

2. The following questions apply to the compound labeled A on the transparency.
   a. What is the name of the compound? **pentanal**
   b. To what category of organic compound (carboxylic acid, ketone, ester, amide, or aldehyde) does it belong? **aldehyde**
   c. State whether you would expect this compound to be polar and whether it can form hydrogen bonds with water. Also, predict whether the compound's boiling point would be lower or higher than that of the alcohol with the same number of carbon atoms. **The compound is polar, it can form hydrogen bonds with water, and its boiling point is lower than that of the corresponding alcohol.**

3. The following questions apply to the compound labeled B on the transparency.
   a. What is the name of the compound? **3-pentanone**
   b. To what category of organic compound does it belong? **ketone**
   c. State whether you would expect this compound to be polar, and whether it can form hydrogen bonds with water. **The compound is polar and can form hydrogen bonds with water.**

4. The following questions apply to the compound labeled C on the transparency.
   a. What is the name of the compound? **pentanoic acid**
   b. To what category of organic compound does it belong? **carboxylic acid**
   c. What are the name and formula of the functional group of compounds in this category? **carboxyl group, –COOH**
   d. State whether you would expect this compound to be polar, whether it would ionize in water, and what the color of litmus paper in the resulting solution would be. **The compound is polar, it ionizes in water, and litmus paper in the resulting solution is red.**

5. What is the name of the ion labeled D? **pentanoate ion**

6. What are the names of the compounds labeled E and F on the transparency? **E is methyl pentanoate. F is pentanamide.**

TEACHING TRANSPARENCY WORKSHEET

Forming Polymers

72

Use with Chapter 23,
Section 23.5

1. Define the following terms.

a. polymer
a large molecule consisting of many repeating subunits

b. monomer
a single unit molecule from which a polymer is made

c. structural unit of a polymer
a repeating group of atoms formed by the bonding of monomers

2. Look at the reaction labeled A, which illustrates a polymerization reaction.

a. What are the name and formula of the monomer? **ethene, C_2H_4**

b. What does the structure labeled *n* in reaction A represent?
the structural unit of the polymer

c. What is the name of the polymer produced? **polyethylene**

d. What kind of polymerization reaction is reaction A: condensation or addition? How can you tell?
Addition; all the atoms in the monomers are retained in the polymer.

3. Look at polymerization reaction B.

a. The first of the monomers shown is called methyl terephthalate. What is the name of the second monomer?
1,2-ethanediol

b. What does the structure labeled *n* in reaction B represent?
the structural unit of the polymer

c. The name of the polymer produced in reaction B is poly(ethylene terephthalate). It is commonly known as Dacron. What is the name of the other product formed?
methanol

d. What kind of polymerization reaction is reaction B: condensation or addition? How can you tell?
Condensation; it occurs with the loss of a small by-product (methanol).

4. Look at polymerization reaction C.

a. The monomer is commonly called vinyl chloride. What is its more formal chemical name?
chloroethene

b. The common abbreviated name of the polymer produced in reaction C is PVC. Of what complete name is PVC an abbreviation?
polyvinyl chloride

TEACHING TRANSPARENCY WORKSHEET

Kinds of Organic Reactions

71

Use with Chapter 23,
Section 23.4

1. What is the name for the category of reaction in which one atom or a group of atoms in a molecule is replaced by another?
a substitution reaction

2. Which two of the reactions labeled A–I are examples of that type of reaction?
E, I

3. Which of these two reactions is also a halogenation reaction?
I

4. What is the name for the category of reaction in which atoms on two adjacent carbon atoms are removed, forming an additional bond between the carbon atoms?
an elimination reaction

5. Which three of the reactions labeled A–I are examples of that type of reaction?
A, D, H

6. Which of these three reactions is also a dehydration reaction?
H

7. Which of these three reactions is also a dehydrogenation reaction?
D

8. What is the name for the category of reaction in which other atoms bond to each of two double-bonded or triple-bonded atoms?
an addition reaction

9. Which three of the reactions labeled A–I are examples of that type of reaction?
B, F, G

10. Which of these three reactions is also a hydration reaction?
B

11. Which of these three reactions is also a hydrogenation reaction?
F

12. What is the name for the category of reaction in which two smaller organic molecules combine to form a more complex molecule, accompanied by the loss of a small molecule such as water?
a condensation reaction

13. Which of the reactions labeled A–I is an example of that type of reaction?
C

TEACHING TRANSPARENCY WORKSHEET

Enzymes

73

Use with Chapter 24,
Section 24.1

1. What is the area labeled X called?
the active site

2. What is Y?
the enzyme-substrate complex

3. What is Z?
the product of the reaction

4. Explain what is happening at each step in the diagram.

Step 1   The substrates bind to the active site of the enzyme. The active site
changes shape slightly to fit more tightly around the substrates.

Step 2   Bonds are broken and new bonds form to produce the product.

5. Compare the shape of the enzyme at the beginning and at the end of the reaction.
The shape of the enzyme is the same.

6. What effect do enzymes have on the following?
a. reaction rate   increase
b. activation energy   decrease

7. How does the large size of enzyme molecules affect their ability to catalyze reactions?
It allows enzymes to form multiple bonds of different types with substrates,
which makes enzymes more effective catalysts.

8. What reaction does the enzyme papain catalyze?
the breakdown of proteins into amino acids

9. Name and describe three functions of proteins in addition to their role as enzymes.
Transport proteins: transport smaller molecules throughout the body.
Structural proteins: form structures vital to organisms. Hormones: carry
signals from one part of the body to another.

TEACHING TRANSPARENCY WORKSHEET

Condensation Reactions

74

Use with Chapter 24,
Sections 24.1–24.3

1. Identify the type of organic compound represented by each of the letters A–F on the transparency.

A   amino acid   D   disaccharide

B   dipeptide   E   fatty acid

C   monosaccharide   F   triglyceride

2. What functional group is represented by the bond that is formed in reaction 1?
amide

3. Where does the water that is formed in reaction 1 come from?
It comes from the OH in the carboxyl group of one amino acid and one of the H
atoms in the amino group of the other amino acid.

4. In reaction 1, is the order in which the two reactants are linked important? Explain.
Yes, the order is important. Reversing the order will produce a different dipeptide.

5. What functional group is represented by the bond that is formed in reaction 2?
ether

6. What is the common name of the three-carbon molecule that reacts with the compounds
labeled E in reaction 3?
glycerol

7. What functional group is represented by the bonds that are formed in reaction 3?
ester

8. Contrast the water-solubility of reaction products D and F. Explain the difference.
D is water soluble because it has multiple hydroxyl groups, which are polar. F
is insoluble in water because it has three long hydrocarbon chains, which are
nonpolar.

TEACHING TRANSPARENCY WORKSHEET

Photosynthesis, Cellular Respiration, and Fermentation

Use with Chapter 24, Section 24.5

75

1. Identify the metabolic processes labeled A–D on the transparency.

   A __photosynthesis__   C __lactic acid fermentation__

   B __cellular respiration__   D __alcoholic fermentation__

2. What kinds of organisms carry out each metabolic process?

   A __plants, algae, and some bacteria__

   B __most organisms__

   C __animals__

   D __yeast and some bacteria__

3. Label each metabolic process as anabolism or catabolism.

   A __anabolism__   C __catabolism__

   B __catabolism__   D __catabolism__

4. Identify the following compounds shown on the transparency.

   $C_6H_{12}O_6$ _____ __glucose__

   $CH_3CH(OH)COOH$ _____ __lactic acid__

   CH_3CH_2OH _____ __ethanol__

5. What provides the energy that is used in process A? __sunlight__

6. Compare the efficiencies of processes B, C, and D in terms of ATP production. __Process B (cellular respiration) produces a maximum of 38 moles of ATP per mole of glucose. Processes C (lactic acid fermentation) and D (alcoholic fermentation) each produce only two moles of ATP per mole of glucose.__

7. Explain how process C is related to some instances of muscle pain and fatigue. __During strenuous exercise, muscle cells use lactic acid fermentation to produce energy. If lactic acid is produced more rapidly than it can be removed by the blood, it accumulates in muscles, causing pain and fatigue.__

8. Describe three commercial applications of process D. __Alcoholic fermentation is used to make bread dough rise, to form tofu from soybeans, and to produce ethanol for gasohol and alcoholic beverages.__

TEACHING TRANSPARENCY WORKSHEET

Production of Transuranium Elements

Use with Chapter 25, Section 25.3

76

1. Does the diagram illustrate a natural transmutation reaction or an induced transmutation reaction? __induced transmutation__

2. What is the name and nuclear symbol of the isotope produced in the reaction? __dubnium-266; $^{266}_{105}Db$__

3. What difficulties do you foresee in trying to carry out the reaction shown here? __Large amounts of energy are needed to make the neon nucleus collide with the americium nucleus. Unstable Am-244 must be prepared before the induced transmutation reaction can be performed.__

4. Write a nuclear equation to show how dubnium-263, lawrencium-262, and seaborgium-266 can be produced from a nuclear reaction of neon-22 and americium-224.

   $^{22}_{10}Ne + ^{244}_{95}Am \rightarrow ^{263}_{105}Db + 3^{1}_{0}n$

   $^{22}_{10}Ne + ^{244}_{95}Am \rightarrow ^{262}_{103}Lr + ^{4}_{2}He$

   $^{22}_{10}Ne + ^{244}_{95}Am \rightarrow ^{266}_{106}Sg + ^{0}_{-1}e$

5. Each of the radioisotopes in the table decays within 20 seconds to 10 hours. Write a nuclear equation for each decay.

   $^{263}_{105}Db \rightarrow ^{0}_{-1}e + ^{263}_{106}Sg$

   $^{262}_{103}Lr + ^{0}_{-1}e \rightarrow ^{262}_{102}No$

   $^{266}_{106}Sg \rightarrow ^{4}_{2}He + ^{262}_{104}Rf$

6. Which, if any, of the four isotopes listed in the table would you expect to find at Earth's surface? Why? __None of the isotopes are likely to be present at Earth's surface because they all have very short half-lives.__

Name _____   Date _____   Class _____

TEACHING TRANSPARENCY WORKSHEET   77

Formation of Ozone

1. What is the source of energy used in the decomposition of the oxygen molecule in step A of this reaction?
ultraviolet radiation from sunlight

2. Why does this step of the reaction take place in the stratosphere but not in higher layers of the atmosphere?
There are fewer oxygen molecules in the higher layers.

3. Why does this step of the reaction not take place in the troposphere?
Not enough high-energy solar radiation penetrates to the troposphere.

4. What do the asterisks on the molecule indicate?
energized molecules

5. Why is the ozone molecule formed in step B of the reaction said to be energized?
It has absorbed energy from the ultraviolet radiation.

6. Name two natural components of the atmosphere represented by the symbol X in step C of this reaction.
nitrogen and oxygen

7. What process is responsible for the reactions shown in steps A and D?
photodissociation

8. Of what importance, if any, is this series of reactions for life on Earth?
This series of reactions produces ozone. The ozone shields the surface of Earth from damaging ultraviolet radiation.

Name _____   Date _____   Class _____

TEACHING TRANSPARENCY WORKSHEET   78

The Water Cycle

1. By what process does water move from lakes and oceans into the atmosphere?
evaporation

2. What is the source of energy that makes this process possible?
solar energy from sunlight

3. In what physical states is water found in the atmosphere?
gas, liquid, and solid

4. Describe the process by which water vapor in the atmosphere becomes precipitation.
Water vapor in the atmosphere cools and condenses as liquid water on dust particles. Water droplets then coalesce to form larger water drops, which fall to Earth as precipitation.

5. Describe what happens to water that falls to Earth's surface as rain.
Some soaks into the ground to form groundwater, while some runs along the surface in the form of runoff.

6. Describe the process by which groundwater returns to the atmosphere.
Groundwater flows through the ground until it reaches a river, a stream, a lake, or an ocean. Eventually it evaporates and becomes water vapor in the atmosphere.

7. How is the composition of groundwater, water vapor, and water in the oceans different?
Groundwater is freshwater and contains relatively few dissolved salts. Ocean water contains large amounts of dissolved salts. Water vapor is a pure compound.

Name _____ Date _____ Class _____

The Nitrogen Cycle

1. What does the term *nitrogen fixation* mean?
Nitrogen fixation is the process by which elementary nitrogen is converted into a
form that can be used by plants.

2. What role does lightning play in the nitrogen cycle? Write the equations that show this.
Lightning provides the energy needed to convert nitrogen and oxygen to
nitrogen oxide: $N_2(g) + O_2(g) \rightarrow 2NO(g)$; $2NO(g) + O_2(g) \rightarrow 2NO_2(g)$

3. What role does rain water play in the nitrogen cycle?
Rain water converts nitrogen dioxide (NO_2) into nitric acid (HNO_3).

4. What role do soil bacteria play in the nitrogen cycle?
Soil bacteria convert nitrogen in the soil first to ammonia (NH_3) and then to
nitrates (NO_3^-).

5. In what form does nitrogen most commonly occur in the atmosphere?
as the diatomic element nitrogen, N_2

6. In what form do green plants take nitrogen from the soil?
in the form of nitrates (NO_3^-)

7. In what form and from what source do animals get nitrogen?
Animals get complex nitrogen compounds from eating plants or other animals.

8. How is nitrogen recycled from living organisms to the atmosphere?
Unused nitrogen compounds are excreted by animals as waste. These wastes are
then converted to elementary nitrogen by microorganisms in the soil.

Name _____ Date _____ Class _____

The Carbon Cycle

1. By what natural processes does carbon dioxide enter Earth's atmosphere?
cellular respiration, decomposition of limestone, decomposition of dead plants
and animals

2. How do human activities affect the amount of carbon dioxide in the atmosphere?
Combustion of fossil fuels results in an increase in the amount of carbon dioxide
in the atmosphere.

3. By what natural processes is carbon dioxide removed from Earth's atmosphere?
photosynthesis and dissolving in surface waters

4. Some carbon is stored in the lithosphere for millions of years. In what forms is it stored
and how does it get there?
Some carbon is stored in the form of fossil fuels, produced by the decay of plants
and animals. Some carbon is stored in the form of limestone, formed from the
shells of dead marine animals.

5. What role do green plants play in the carbon cycle?
Green plants convert carbon dioxide in the atmosphere to carbohydrates by
means of photosynthesis. They also return carbon dioxide to the atmosphere in
the process of cellular respiration and, after they have died, as a result of decay.

6. What role do animals play in the carbon cycle?
Animals convert the carbohydrates from plants and other animals into complex
carbon-containing compounds. They return carbon dioxide to the atmosphere in
the process of cellular respiration and, after they have died, as a result of decay.

7. What role do marine animals play in the carbon cycle?
Marine animals convert carbon dioxide dissolved in seawater into shells and other
hard body parts that may later be converted into limestone. They also return
carbon dioxide to the atmosphere in the process of cellular respiration and, after
they have died, as a result of decay.

CREDITS

Art Credits

1 (TT 1) Glencoe; **3 (TT 2)** Glencoe; **7 (TT 4)** Navta Associates; **9 (TT 5)** Navta Associates; **11 (TT 6)** Navta Associates; **13 (TT 7)** MacArt Design; **17 (TT 9)** Glencoe; **19 (TT 10)** MacArt Design; **21 (TT 11)** Glencoe; **23 (TT 12)** Glencoe; **25 (TT 13)** Glencoe; **27 (TT 14)** MacArt Design; **29 (TT 15)** Glencoe; **31 (TT 16)** Glencoe; **33 (TT 17)** Glencoe; **35 (TT 18)** Glencoe; **37 (TT 19)** Glencoe; **39 (TT 20)** Glencoe; **41 (TT 21)** Glencoe; **43 (TT 22)** MacArt Design; **45 (TT 23)** MacArt Design; **47 (TT 24)** Glencoe; **49 (TT 25)** MacArt Design; **51 (TT 26)** MacArt Design; **53 (TT 27)** MacArt Design; **55 (TT 28)** MacArt Design; **57 (TT 29)** MacArt Design; **59 (TT 30)** MacArt Design; **61 (TT 31)** MacArt Design; **63 (TT 32)** Navta Associates; **73 (TT 37)** Glencoe; **75 (TT 38)** Glencoe; **77 (TT 39)** Glencoe; **79 (TT 40)** Glencoe; **81 (TT 41)** Glencoe; **83 (TT 42)** Navta Associates; **85 (TT 43)** Navta Associates; **87 (TT 44)** Glencoe; **89 (TT 45)** Glencoe; **91 (TT 46)** Glencoe; **93 (TT 47)** Glencoe; **95 (TT 49)** MacArt Design; **99 (TT 50)** Navta Associates; **103 (TT 52)** Navta Associates; **107 (TT 54)** Navta Associates; **113 (TT 57)** Glencoe; **115 (TT 58)** Glencoe; **117 (TT 59)** Glencoe; **119 (TT 60)** MacArt Design; **125 (TT 63)** Glencoe; **127 (TT 64)** Glencoe; **129 (TT 65)** Glencoe; **131 (TT 66)** Navta Associates; **133 (TT 67)** Glencoe; **135 (TT 68)** Navta Associates; **137 (TT 69)** Navta Associates; **139 (TT 70)** Navta Associates; **141 (TT 71)** Navta Associates; **143 (TT 72)** Navta Associates; **145 (TT 73)** Glencoe; **147 (TT 75)** MacArt Design; **151 (TT 76)** MacArt Design; **153 (TT 77)** MacArt Design; **155 (TT 78)** MacArt Design; **157 (TT 79)** Glencoe; **159 (TT 80)** Glencoe

Photo Credits

5 (TT 3) Jonathan Nourok/PhotoEdit; **7 (TT 4)** Corbis; **15 (TT 8)** Richard Megna/Fundamental Photographs; **101 (TT 51)** Richard Megna/Fundamental Photographs